DATE LOANED

E	NOV 27 '72			PE
	JAN 13 '76			
	APR 29 '82			
GAYLORD 3563			PRINTED IN U.S.A.	

Ernst Benz, a member of the Academy of Sciences and Literature in Mainz, Germany, and co-editor of the leading man journal on the history of religion, *Zeitschrift für Re-* *ns und Geistesgeschichte,* has since 1935 been Professor urch and Dogmatic History at the Philip University at Marburg on the Lahn. A founder-director of the Ecumenical Institute at the University of Marburg, he taught Church History at the Harvard Divinity School in 1960 as a visiting professor. He is a foreign honorary member of the American Academy of Arts and Sciences, Boston, Massachusetts.

EVOLUTION AND CHRISTIAN HOPE:

*Man's Concept of the
Future from the Early Fathers to
Teilhard de Chardin*

ERNST BENZ

*Translated from the German by
Heinz G. Frank*

ANCHOR BOOKS
DOUBLEDAY & COMPANY, INC.
Garden City, New York

Evolution and Christian Hope *was originally published by Double-day & Company, Inc., 1966. The Anchor Books Edition is published by arrangement with Nymphenburger Verlagshandlung, Munich, Germany.*

Anchor Books edition: 1968

CONTENTS

INTRODUCTION

For a number of years theologians have been grappling with the problems of demythologizing, but it appears now that there isn't much more to be gained from worrying this dry bone, and a shift of emphasis is clearly in evidence. In fact, the shift toward new problems has been forced upon students of theology by the momentous changes in the sciences of anthropology and cosmology - changes of a nature that cannot be ignored. Above all, these are changes that have occurred since the evolution theory has come to prevail in the natural sciences.

In contrast to the theological concept that man as a fully developed being was placed into a fully developed world like a tenant who moved, with a duly signed lease, into a newly completed, prefabricated apartment, anthropology and cosmology have come to the conclusion that not only is man himself, as a species, part of an immeasurably long chain in life's development, but also that contemporary man is still going through a constant development in consciousness. Furthermore, man is not only transforming his environment; he also exercises a direct influence on his own continuing evolution. It is this image of a changing man in a changing world, a world transformed by man, that can no longer be ignored by theology.

During a period when existentialist philosophers and theologians were increasingly writing off history in favor of a dialectics of the moment, anthropology has been opening new dimensions of history: It has explored thousands and hundreds of thousands of years of early history and prehistory; it has thrown light upon the development of man from prehuman and near-human animal to his appearance as *homo sapiens*.

During a period when theologians, concerned with the problem of existential decision in the present, had forgotten to inquire into the meaning of the future, the natural sciences, on their own behalf, have asked the question of man's future with an intensity that is astounding—because, indeed, our present knowledge of man's past development forces the question of man's future right into the foreground.

Hope was the original impulse of theology. But it abandoned it to secular movements like Marxism and communism. Instead, it became absorbed in contemplating the relationship between existence and death and became fascinated by the problems of evil and original sin. Anthropology, a natural science, is now restoring hope to its rightful place.

As has happened before, the changes in theology were initiated by a few outsiders. Within the German sphere, the changes were indicated by thinkers such as Leopold Ziegler. In a late work *Das Lehrgespräch vom allgemeinen Menschen*,[1] he tried to confront the Christian image of man with the findings of modern, scientific anthropology and biology. Similarly, Paul Schütz[2] may be considered a great stimulating force for modern theological thinking. In his critique of existentialism and dialectical theology, he tries to regain for theology the lost categories of hope and prophecy.

The decisive impulse, however, came from the French Jesuit Teilhard de Chardin.[3] An outsider among theologians, a paleoanthropologist by profession, he tried to find a Christian interpretation for the modern, evolutionary world view and to reconcile his vision of the rise of the "human phenomenon" with the development of life and consciousness in a Christian, total understanding of reality. Thus Teilhard provided a new vision of creation, salvation, and eschatology seen in the light of the evolutionary concept.

It is the emergence of this new aspect in theological thinking that gave impulse to the writing of this brief and, by necessity fragmentary, study of the Christian concepts of creation and eschatology as they have changed throughout history. Also included in this survey are the various secularized forms of eschatological hope evolved, more recently, into social and political utopias, expressing in extra-ecclesiastical and partly anti-ecclesiastical terms the impulses of hope and prophecy long neglected and even abandoned by the Church. Especially, however, we shall direct our attention to the origin of the evolution theory as found in the Christian understanding of history and the Christian expectation of the end of time.

In the Christian interpretation of reality, creation and the history of salvation are closely linked. God, the Creator, is the Lord of world history. He leads his creation toward a distinct goal of salvation—this is the fundamental premise of the Christian faith. Creation itself is adapted to man, whom God has created in his image, as a companion in his kingdom. But a meaningful personal relationship between God and man is only possible, where man freely responds to the love of God with his own love. Thus the kingdom of love and freedom is the ultimate goal, in which the Kingdom of God is to be realized and in which creation is to be brought to its culmination.

I

The Expectation of the End of Time in the Early Church

If we try to visualize the expectation of the end of time in the earliest Christian communities of the New Testament period, we encounter a most unexpected situation. On the one hand, we see that all communities were most strongly dominated in their actions and thinking by the expectation of the nearness of the Kingdom of God and by their effort to bring about its immediate advent by prayer. On the other hand, it is impossible to discern a consistent view of the nature of this Kingdom of God, the manner of its advent, or its duration. The expectations were exceedingly manifold and fluid, and there is no way to compress them into a uniform system.[1]

To understand this diversity, we must remember that Christian expectations of the Kingdom of God were derived from the quite varied messianic promises of Judaism. In late Judaism, particularly in the last centuries before the coming of Jesus, these promises were changed and clearly differentiated. We can distinguish two basic types.

(1) The ancient Jewish concept of the fulfillment of salvation-history is dominated by the idea that, at the end of the history of the Jewish people, the Messiah, of the house of David, will come and establish the Kingdom of God. This messianic kingdom is secular, and its expectation therefore has a distinctly political character. It is an empire into which the Anointed of the Lord will gather the tribes of the Chosen People. From Jerusalem, he will establish a world kingdom of peace into which

other nations will be incorporated, either by being forced into subjection or by joining voluntarily.[2]

This expectation of a secular messianic empire stirred the hearts of the Jews of the last pre-Christian centuries even more strongly since their attempts to establish political independence in their own state repeatedly suffered bloody suppression. The expectation of a secular Messiah, who would be the founder of a Jewish kingdom, became the strongest impulse for political revolutions, particularly against Hellenistic and Roman rule. Even when the great period of the Maccabean uprising against the rule of the Seleucids was over, and the Jewish dream of freedom appeared to have been broken, the longing for freedom lived on in the people's hearts.

The time before the coming of Jesus was filled with a succession of messianic insurrections. A number of new personalities, pretending to be Messiah and claiming messianic powers for themselves and for the battle of liberation, came to the fore. One of them was Felix the Egyptian, who led his adherents to the Mount of Olives, in the expectation that, at his command, the walls of Jerusalem would collapse and make way for his triumphal entry into the city. Another messianic insurgent led his faithful into the desert, reminding them that, according to the prophets, God had promised to establish in the desert a miraculous place of salvation for his faithful.

Groups of insurgents sprang up, particularly in Galilee. The more hopeless the present, the more ardent was their hope for a better future. They were called robbers—*lestai* —but they accepted this name as a title of honor. A band numbering thousands surreptitiously stirred up the fight for a national Jewish kingdom and the national Messiah for whom they yearned and prayed. Thus insurrections which were suppressed by force occurred again and again. The last of these bands of freedom-fighters perished in Masada, where its members killed themselves and their families, 960 men and women, to avoid being captured alive by the Romans.

The existence of this political messianism must be counted an important factor when we try to understand the momentary success of Jesus at the time of his solemn entry into Jerusalem.[3] His entry stirred up general enthusiasm. The people thought that the longed-for hero of political liberation had arrived, and he was joyfully received. They expected him to take decisive political action which would bring the fulfillment of national expectations, and their frustration was all the greater when his arrival had no effect. Jesus foiled the hopes of these popular groups by refusing to become a political Messiah.

On the other hand, his opponents took advantage of this misrepresentation of his person in order to destroy him. The Pharisees and the priests of the Temple presented his appearance to the Roman occupation authorities as a messianic insurrection. They accused him of a political crime, punishable by death; he was, then, convicted and executed as a Jewish insurgent who had rebelled against the authority of the Roman state. The inscription on the Cross—Jesus of Nazareth, King of the Jews—is evidence that the official reason for his conviction and execution was his revolt as a Jewish Messiah King against the authority of Rome.[4]

(2) But there is, side by side with this political messianic hope, a completely different form of the expectation of the end of time. It was maintained by a community of pious people who clung to this hope with deep fervor and ardent fanaticism. This second type of expectation of the Messiah and of the Kingdom of God is represented by some groups of the poor in the land, pietistic communities such as those of Enoch, of the Essenes, and of Qumran on the Dead Sea. They did not long for a secular Messiah but for the Anointed of the Lord who would bring them the divine rather than the secular Kingdom.

In these circles, the feeling prevailed that the end of the world was at hand; that the old aeon was passing away and the new one was about to dawn; that fulfillment would not come in the old world, but in a future, coming one, and for that one must prepare by penitence.

These pious people abhorred the sword and the struggle, insurrections and rebellions. They believed that all man can do is to prepare his soul for the coming events. Nothing but the miraculous power of God can create the new age. Its birth will be preceded by tremendous messianic labor pains and a fearful judgment over the godless, the pagans, Satan, and his demonic powers. For them, the Messiah does not ascend the Davidic throne as a secular king of the house of David, but as a heavenly figure, as the Son of God, who will rule the world, and who, after overcoming all earthly and supernatural demonic powers, will put the whole cosmos at God's feet.

Significantly enough, the transformation of the old nationalistic expectation of the Messiah and the Kingdom of God did not occur until late in Judaism; it came as the result of its contact with the Aryan, Zoroastrian religion during the Persian exile. This was proved convincingly by Rudolf Otto in his book *Reich Gottes und Menschensohn.*[5] The idea of a heavenly Kingdom animated the religion of Zarathustra. This is where the expectation of the Son of Man came from. He was the primal man, the primeval spiritual being, the Son of God, the spirit of light, who descends to earth to redeem all men and to lead them toward a new, glorious age.

The older Jewish expectation of the Messiah now becomes fused with this expectation of the coming Son of Man. The Messiah is no longer a man of this world. As the books of Enoch describe him, he has become a divine being, who lives throughout the ages. He descends to the world of evil to gather his faithful and lead them back into the dominion of light.

This transcendental version of the old expectation has another new facet. According to the older Jewish expectation of the end of time, only those who belonged to the last generation of mankind would benefit from the divine transformation of the world. They would be fortunate enough to live in this world at the time of the coming of the Messiah. All previous generations had languished for this consummation of their hopes, but they faded away and did not live to see it. Only the last generation of the faithful would find this fulfillment here, on this earth, and they would be the beneficiaries of the entire earlier development of mankind.

But now, a new Zoroastrian element enters into the Jewish expectation: the hope of resurrection.[6] In ancient Judaism the hope for a continuation of life after death and belief in resurrection were unknown. Now, the expectation of the Kingdom of God assumes a transcendental character, and the Persian hope of resurrection is accepted as well. At the resurrection, the Kingdom of God will comprise all the faithful of all the generations of mankind. The faithful of earlier generations have not died in vain; they will find the fulfillment of their faith in resurrection.

In the new age, the Messiah-Son of Man will rule over the faithful of all times and of all nations. Thus the expectation of the end of time is rather significantly free of restrictions. It no longer concerns the Jews exclusively, although they are the true carriers of the divine promise. With its transcendental character, this expectation now assumes a universalist character as well.

Jesus himself appeared in Galilee as an itinerant preacher of repentance. Actually, similar figures were nothing new to the faithful of late Judaism. Just before his coming, a man had appeared who resembled him in many respects, namely, John the Baptist. If we compare their sermons superficially, we are struck by their extraor-

dinary resemblance. Both of them preached that the
Kingdom of God was at hand, both connected this
prophecy with an appeal for penitence, and both addressed their proclamations to those faithful whose entire
faith and hope was concentrated upon the coming of the
Kingdom of God. These faithful did not await a this-
worldly political empire. They yearned for the advent and
miraculous unfolding of a celestial empire which will
transform the earth. The one who brings in this divine
empire will gather its true and chosen citizens into it,
and this realm of miracles will bear witness to the power
of God, be the realm of God's truth and justice. It is necessary to prepare for this Kingdom now, to pave the road
now for the Master who is coming. Injustice must be
swept out now so that the one who brings the Kingdom
of God may find open hearts and consecrated disciples.

Yet there was a gap between Jesus and John which
could not be bridged. John was a preacher of repentance.
He pointed to the Kingdom of God and to the one who
would bring it. He asked for penitence. In him, the consciousness of history and the expectation of the end of
time which had been the prophets' came to life again for
the last time and in a most intensive form. He fanned
the hope of fulfillment until it was white-hot; he forced
men into an attitude which made them ignore the
troubles of their time and concentrate entirely on imminent fulfillment. But he did not bring fulfillment itself.

From the very beginning, Jesus had a completely
different understanding of his mission. He knew that he
would bring fulfillment himself, that God and the miraculous powers of the Kingdom of God were already
present and at work within him. He proclaimed the
joyous message that the long-promised Kingdom was
near, that its powers began to become effective, that fulfillment had come. This was the new idea: the promised

Kingdom is not of this world but lies in the future. The new aeon comes, out of the future, to intervene in the present. From the next world, it brings salvation to this world. It is a divine *dynamis,* salvation breaking in, a living charismatic reality which forges humanity into a new community.

It is of decisive importance that Jesus did not simply transfer to his person the promise of the coming of the heavenly Son of Man, as Enoch had expressed it. He also gave a different interpretation to this expectation of the Son of Man. Pious Jewish circles, such as the Enoch community and other pietistic, apocalyptic groups, expected the Son of Man to appear as a figure of light, from above. Wielding the power of God, he would break into this world, accompanied by the angels of heaven. His breath alone would vanquish the enemies of the Lord and reduce them to no more than his footstool. He would thus be a divine conqueror and triumphant victor who would appear on the scene with all the symbols of divine power and sovereignty.

But for Jesus, the expectation of the Son of Man is associated with a totally different image, namely, with that of the Suffering Servant of God. The Son of Man does not make his entry into the world as a triumphant victor. As the Suffering Servant, he lives in this world in humility and poverty, he delves deeply into all the sufferings of the world, offers his life for the sins of humanity, and suffers death. Only after he has experienced all the pains of human existence, will he reach the state of glory, be raised, and transfigured into the real figure of light of the Son of Man. Then, he will return in glory to establish the Kingdom.

Thus Jesus reinterpreted the figure of the Son of Man and conceived his mission. His own actions and attitudes are determined accordingly, for he knows that he has received the call to carry out his saving mission on two levels. First, he must endure the fate of the Suffering Servant and hidden Son of God in humility and misery. He must offer his life to atone for humanity's sins, and he must accept death. Then, he will come into his glory, be raised and, as Son of Man, sit at God's right hand.

The peculiar character of the specifically Christian understanding of history is based on these premises. On the one hand, it is consciousness of fulfillment. The old promises of the coming Saviour and of the coming of salvation have become reality in Jesus Christ—the time has been fulfilled. On the other hand, this fulfillment is not complete. In Jesus Christ, the first-born from the dead, the first to have been raised, it has only started.

The vital forces of the new aeon have appeared within the old one. They drive on toward their complete manifestation and glorification. The fullness of salvation will not come to pass until the Lord comes a second time, in glory. Then he will celebrate the great nuptial supper with his followers and partake of it with them.

The different categories of the hope for salvation were not clearly divided. They intersected and became mixed in a variety of ways. Under the influence of the persecutions which the disciples of Jesus suffered after his death, a peculiar duplication of the expectation of the end of time developed.[7] Paul and the author of the book of Revelation reveal the expectation that, (1) faithful Christians will rule the world for a while with their Master after his return. This refers to those Christians who happen to be alive then. The dead will then be raised and share in his Kingdom on this earth. (2) Only after the completion of this first act of the events which lead to the end of time will there be a general resurrection of the dead, followed by the Last Judgment at which the chosen will participate as judges.

In Revelation, this expectation is given a more concrete form in the idea of the thousand-year Kingdom. An angel will come from heaven and chain the dragon, "the ancient serpent who is the Devil and Satan," for a thousand years. The dragon will then be thrown into the bottomless pit and sealed there, so that for a thousand years he will be unable to lead the pagans astray. Then it continues:

> Then I saw thrones, and seated on them were those to whom judgment was committed. Also I saw the souls of those who had been beheaded for their testimony to Jesus and for the word of God, and who had not worshiped the beast or its image and had not received its mark on their foreheads or their hands. They came to life again, and reigned with Christ a thousand years. The rest of the dead did not come to life again until the thousand years were ended. This is the first resurrection. Blessed and holy is he who shares in the first resurrection! Over such the second death has no power, but they shall be priests of God and of Christ, and they shall reign with him a thousand years.   (Rev. 20:4-6)

Only after that period will the dead be raised, the Last Judgment, the creation of a new heaven and a new earth, and the advent of the heavenly Jerusalem take place. According to Revelation, the thousand-year Kingdom will be a kingdom of the privileged chosen ones. In it, this elect fellowship, particularly the martyrs and all those who have remained steadfast during the time of persecution, will be rewarded by a special status.

It is this promise which had a revolutionary effect on the course of church history. The status of the thousand-year Kingdom is of an intermediate character. This is not only due to its chronological position between its present, this-earthly status and the status resulting from the Last Judgment, but it also has an intermediate status in terms of its contents.

In the early Church the expectation of the Millennium had assumed the character of a social and political utopia. It was understood to be a state in which the chosen Christians reigned over the earth together with their Master. Repeatedly, in the course of church history, this hope for the Millennium gave impetus to ecclesiastical, political, and social reform movements and revolutions. It is understandable that the first part of this expectation —namely, the establishment of a kingdom in which the chosen would reign with Christ, in which they would become ministers and judges or assume other positions of leadership—held a much stronger fascination for religious hopes and for social and political imagination than the second one which dealt with the "Last Judgment."

The Millennium is closer to religious concepts and imagination than the Last Judgment. It is more palpable. It gives concrete ideas to hope and imagination, and has a strong and immediate effect upon the emotions. In the early Church, the expectation of the Millennium is connected with the expectation of the coming of Paradise, of a golden age. In the earliest period of Christianity, the motives of the social and religious utopias became mixed occasionally with those of the fool's paradise which is one of the original concepts of a social utopia: The fulfillment of the wishful dream of total satisfaction without work or effort.

Bishop Papias of Hierapolis ascribed the following quotation to Jesus himself:

> There will be days when vines will grow of which each will have ten times one thousand boughs. Each bough will have ten times one thousand branches and each branch ten times one thousand tendrils. Each tendril will have ten times one thousand clusters of grapes and each cluster will have ten times one thousand grapes. When pressed each grape will

yield twenty-five barrels of wine. If one of the saints will pluck a grape, another grape will exclaim: "I am better, take me, praise the Lord through me."

Likewise will a kernel of wheat produce ten times one thousand ears, and each ear will have ten times one thousand kernels and each kernel will contain ten pounds of fine, white flour. Other plants will also produce fruit, seeds, and stalks with the same abundance. All animals who only live off the bounty of the earth will live together peacefully, serving man in complete obedience.[8]

This orientation toward a time of salvation which has already begun has a very disturbing and hastening effect. The basic premise is that the present time is understood as the end of time. God, the Creator of the world and Lord of history, drives world history rapidly to its end. The principal event, which initiated the end, has already happened. It is the coming of the Son, through whom God has "in these last days spoken to us" (Heb. 1:2). In this situation, the community is not satisfied merely with confident "waiting." It tries to hasten the coming of fulfillment in many ways.

The first of these is through prayer. In its Eucharistic service, the community prays in fervent supplication for the end of the world. The prayer culminates in the cry: "Come, Lord!" Two thousand years later, this cry sounds rather conventional to us. But originally it was a conjuring call to the risen Master, an imploring plea that the Lord not delay his return any longer, that he come very soon, indeed now, immediately. The prayer, "Come, Lord," is a prayer for a quick end of the world.

According to the Didache, the community offers this prayer during Holy Communion: "Let grace come and let this world pass away. Hosanna to the God of David!

If anyone is holy, let him come. If not, let him repent. Maranatha."[9]

Thus the community prays to Christ to hasten the end of the world and to bring about, as quickly as possible, the new age in which the children of the Kingdom will sit at table and reign with the Son of Man. One prayer begs that the Kingdom of God come soon and that the messianic meal with the returned Son of Man be continued in glory. The other one expresses the hope that the old world disappear quickly since it bars the way to his coming. The impulses in the two prayers are closely linked.

The second element is prophetic vision. He who is filled with the Holy Ghost can see coming events now. Vision leaps over the present and anticipates the future. It already sees coming fulfillment. Whatever has been longed and prayed for, is seen as reality.

The author of the book of Revelation sees the bridegroom say to the bride: "Come." He already sees the coming of the heavenly Jerusalem, recognizes its gates and streets, and the spring of living water which flows among the trees of Paradise (Rev. 22:1ff.). Stephen, the dying martyr, sees heaven opened and the Son of Man standing at God's right hand (Acts 7:55 f.). The hastening effect of prophetic vision is extraordinary since it transforms the longings of the faithful into palpable reality right in front of their eyes.

The third element is asceticism. Asceticism is an anticipation of early fulfillment, an adjustment to coming events by anticipating them here and now. It hastens the end of the present age and the coming of the new one. In the Kingdom of God, there will be no marriage, nor will there be any giving in marriage. Sexuality has been overcome (Mt. 22:30). For Paul, marriage is a license valid only for this age, meant only for people who cannot manage to adjust radically to the new one (I Cor.

7:7 ff.). Celibacy is not only an anticipation of impending perfection, but also a way to enforce it. By renouncing marriage and giving up the sexual life, we help to bring the old age to an end.

Asceticism is a transition to active abolition of the old aeon. It is a means to hasten the end of the world. What is considered normal in the present age is studiously ignored. Compromises are avoided, if possible, and only reluctantly allowed on an individual basis, to accommodate the "weak." Martyrs and ascetics force the hastening of the coming of fulfillment. As Tertullian writes: "The Holy Scripture has clearly established the time of consummation of all our hopes so that we should not believe that it could become reality unless Christ returns. Our wishes and sighs, therefore, plead for an end of this age so that, after this world is gone, the great day of the Lord may come, the day of wrath and retribution."[10]

It must be generally assumed that until the middle of the second century, at least in the Church of Asia Minor, hope for the end of the world and expectation of the early coming of the Kingdom were still vibrant parts of the Christian faith. Every Sunday, in the Thanksgiving prayers of the service of Holy Communion, words referring to the expectation of the Kingdom and the return of Christ were spoken, as earlier, with deep fervor. This must have helped keep them alive in the hearts of the faithful.

Side by side with this, another pattern may also be found in the New Testament. It knows of a progressive development in salvation-history, a gradual growth of the Kingdom of God in history. This pattern is indicated already in the Gospel of John, where it is connected with the doctrine of the Holy Ghost. John has a special concept of the work of the Spirit at the end of time. According to the report of this evangelist (7:39), Jesus had emphasized that the Spirit had not yet come. This interpretation meant that successive, chronologically separate ages were assigned to the Son and the Holy Spirit for their parts in the history of salvation on this earth. It is stressed that during the age in which the Son—the Word made flesh—carries out his mission on earth, the Spirit will not have arrived. Jesus himself promises its coming, but only after he has returned to the Father. The Holy Ghost will then take the place of Jesus on earth as the Intercessor (the Paraclete) of the remaining community (14:26).

There is an explicit description of the act by which the Lord, after his resurrection, fulfills his promise of the coming of the Spirit. Before his ascension, he imparts the Holy Spirit to his disciples through his breath: "Jesus said to them again, 'Peace be with you. As the Father has sent me, even so I send you.' And when he had said this, he breathed on them and said to them, 'Receive the Holy Spirit. If you forgive the sins of any, they are forgiven; if you retain the sins of any, they are retained'" (Jn. 20: 21–23).

For John, the ascension concludes the period of the Son's work on earth. A new age begins, that of the work of the Holy Spirit for the salvation of the community remaining on this earth.

This also explains another expectation, which could hardly be understood once Christianity reached the ecclesiastical stage, namely, that the strength of the spirit of the disciples will go beyond the measure of strength which Jesus showed during his lifetime by miracles and other evidences of power. Jesus promised his disciples such an increase in spiritual strength that it would surpass even the power at work within him. In John 14:12 f., he said in his valedictory to his disciples: "Truly, truly, I say to you, he who believes in me will also do the works that I do; and greater works than these will he do, because I go to the Father. Whatever you ask in my name,

I will do it, that the Father may be glorified in the Son."

Here Jesus asked his disciples not to be too modest in their pleas. His own miracles should be the measure of their pleas to the Father. The spiritual power of Christians shall not be restricted by the extent of the spiritual power which Jesus realized in his lifetime. Not even the Word incarnate is the measure of the spiritual power which will be at work within Christianity in the time after his ascension, the age of the Paraclete. To glorify the Father through the Son, Christ promised a miraculous power which would enable them to perform greater works than he had himself performed. His works would be surpassed by the greater works of the Holy Ghost.

Expectations of a similar exaltation in connection with events at the end of time are also expressed in the first letter of John (3:2): "Beloved, we are God's children now; it does not yet appear what we shall be, but we know that when he appears we shall be like him, for we shall see him as he is." Here too, we find a reference to different stages of the exaltation of existence. Faithful Christians have become children of light, children of God. But this high stage does not yet represent the supreme one. This last stage has not appeared yet, but Christians know that it will be a new, unimaginable exaltation of existence, up to a level of equality with the returning of Christ.

Paul also had a clear concept of the exaltation of existence brought about by the Spirit. The Spirit does not work only once. A perpetual creative power emanates from it which uplifts and transfigures man, step by step. In his second letter to the Corinthians (4:16), the apostle writes: "Though our outer nature is wasting away, our inner nature is renewed every day." This renewal is not the perpetual restoration of a state of salvation, lost by a new fall. It is rather the progress of the inner man on a path which opens ever higher glory to him. This is shown in the letter, directed to the same community (II Cor. 3:18): "And we all, with unveiled face, beholding the glory of the Lord, are being changed into his likeness from one degree of glory to another, for this comes from the Lord who is the Spirit." Here the Spirit appears as a force which lifts human existence to a superhuman level.

John's concept of the coming of the Paraclete contains the roots of a theology of history which was destined to have repeated revolutionary effects in the future. From the Acts of the Apostles and the letters of Paul it can be seen that a spontaneous eruption of the various gifts of the Spirit dominated the life of the Christian (mostly Hellenistic, pagan-Christian) communities.

At the end of the first century events were summarized in retrospect as follows: "Salvation was declared at first by the Lord, and it was attested to us by those who heard him, while God also bore witness by signs and wonders and various miracles and by gifts of the Holy Spirit distributed according to his own will" (Heb. 2:3).

For Irenaeus, Bishop of Lyons in A.D. 178, the general diffusion of these gifts of God, including the gift of raising the dead, was a most important proof for the truth of the Christian message. It was possible for him to use it when arguing with his pagan and Jewish opponents.

The Montanist movement, which in the beginning of the second century was directed against the institutionalization and secularization of the Church, carried on the Johannine doctrine of the Paraclete. In Montanism, the original Christian expectation that the end of time was near came again to the fore. It was connected directly with John's promise of the coming of the Paraclete. For the religious consciousness of these Montanist communities it is significant to note that they were certain of living in the age of the Paraclete. It was the last period of the history of salvation and preceded the events of the end of time (general resurrection and Last Judgment). Montanus and his communities considered themselves part of the age in the history of salvation which is ruled by the Paraclete. His influence manifested itself in their midst by new evidences of charismatic gifts. This referred particularly to gifts of prophecy and heroic overcoming of the world by radical asceticism and joyful acceptance of martyrdom. For the members of those communities, their prophets Montanus, Prisca, and Maximilla spoke for the Paraclete.

Montanus considered himself the instrument of the Paraclete. This is indicated in his prophecy in which the Paraclete says: "Behold, man is like a lyre and I fly to him like a plectrum. Man sleeps and I keep vigil. Behold, he is the Lord who takes away the hearts of men and gives them new ones." The following proclamation, which Montanus attributed to the Paraclete, throws light also upon his own messianic consciousness: "I, the Lord and Almighty God take my residence in man." Didymus of Alexandria reports another statement of Montanus: "I am the Father and the Son and the Paraclete."[11]

Montanus and his community, therefore, believed that the promise of the Paraclete's coming, given in the Gospel of John, had been fulfilled in them, that the age of the Paraclete had already begun. Their concept of the history of salvation was determined by the principle of development and progress: the end of time brings more gifts of salvation than previous times; it also demands a higher level of ethics, a more radical asceticism, and a more perfect sanctity.

Montanus thus shows an attitude which was quite widespread in early Christian communities but which was abandoned later under the pressure of a certain theology: the abundance of God's grace developing within the history of salvation itself.

It is significant for Montanus' renewal of the concept

of the awakening of the Spirit that he chose the idea of the creative exaltation of man through the Spirit. He made it the focal point of his doctrine of efficacy and sanctification through the Spirit. By his prophecies, Montanus has extended the old Christian postulates for sanctification to their most radical form. He has also set the highest possible goal for sanctification through the Holy Ghost. He was the first to create the concept of a superman as part of his doctrine of sanctity.

Epiphanius, a father of the Church, reports on the prophecies of Montanus which were accessible to him and in which the Paraclete is quoted as follows: "Why do you call superman a man who has been saved? The Paraclete says that the just will shine a hundred times more strongly than the sun, and the small ones among you who have been saved will shine a hundred times more strongly than the moon."[12]

The concept of a superman implies Montanus' rejection of any purely restorative concept of salvation. The salvation by the gifts of the Spirit which man will receive at the end of time will raise him to the level of the superman. This promise of salvation by the Paraclete, reported here by Montanus, surpasses even the promise of Jesus in the Gospel of Matthew. There Jesus assures the just that they will "shine like the sun." But it can be compared with the promise of Jesus in the Gospel of John where he assures his disciples that they will do greater works than he did himself. The "just" signifies here the preferred bearer of the Spirit while the "small ones" are the simple faithful of the sect. The charismatic person is here called "superman." In other quotations of Montanus, he is even given the distinction of being equal with God: he is not one of those who have been saved. This concept is rejected as not applicable.

Hennecke, the editor of the *New Testament Apocrypha*, makes the following comments on this quotation:

"Such hyperbolic expressions were part of the tendencies of that time. It was a doubtful approximation of Christian thinking and pagan ideas which aimed toward the highest aristocratic status instead of working for the formation of the simple Christian personality. Despite the different meaning, there is a strong similarity to Nietzsche."[13]

This remark is not correct from a historical point of view. It projects the modern Protestant ideal of the "formation of the simple Christian personality" upon the early Church. But this is not applicable at all. On the contrary, we can see that charismatic experiences lead to the highest, most exalted expression of Christian self-consciousness. The idea of the superman is a genuinely Christian idea, developed by charismatic persons. By their spiritual experience, they were raised to an unimaginable extent above the level of normal men. In this they saw the work of the grace of God and of the Spirit.

II

A Reinterpretation of the Eschatology of the Early Church

What happened to this radical eschatological attitude?

The answer to this question has led to a rather lively discussion on the origin of the early Catholic Church and early Christian dogma. None less than Albert Schweitzer was the originator of this discussion. From his extensive study of New Testament texts he came to the conclusion that Jesus was entirely under the influence of late Jewish expectations of the end of time and that his thinking was "entirely eschatological." He concluded his *Geschichte der Leben-Jesu-Forschung* with this remark: "It is characteristic for Jesus that, beyond the perfection and salvation of the individual, he looks for the perfection and salvation of the world, and a chosen humanity. He is filled with and determined by the hope and desire for the Kingdom of God."[1]

In his book *The Mysticism of Paul the Apostle*, he pointed out that Jesus was completely imbued with the Son of Man eschatology of the books of Daniel and Enoch. He proclaimed that the Son of Man would come on the clouds of heaven, surrounded by angels. Instead of referring to a messianic kingdom, he referred to a Kingdom of God, which he conceived in entirely supernatural terms. In this Kingdom, the chosen of all generations of humanity will live under the rule of the Son of Man as they would after their resurrection.[2]

According to Schweitzer, the great and decisive crisis in the oldest period of early Christianity came when this expectation of the advent of the Kingdom of God and

of its messianic bearer was not realized. The great crisis
of the early Church resulted from the fact that the
Parousia had not come to pass, that the return of Christ,
announced for the immediate future, had been delayed.
For those who had been baptized died, as also did the
apostles. For those who considered themselves the elect
community, the chosen citizens of the Kingdom waiting
for its advent had to continue living in this world. They
had to adjust to life in the old aeon.

Its own historical experience thus forced the community to drop this thought pattern of eschatological
expectation for the near future. Instead, it had to reinterpret the message of Jesus. The early pattern of expectation had been refuted by history itself since Christ had
not returned and must be replaced by another one. This
other pattern is the reinterpretation of the Christian
message in the light of mysticism and of the Hellenistic
metaphysics of substance.

Albert Schweitzer pointed out, in his book on Paul,
how this apostle initiated a profound reinterpretation of
the old expectation of the end of time. With a gradual
withdrawal from the old pattern, a transformation into a
Christ-mysticism takes place which reaches its conclusion
in John. "Being in Christ" takes the place of the coming
of Christ.[3]

This is the starting point of the great discussion on the
origin of dogma which, to this day, has not been concluded. In his *History of Dogma*, classic in the modern
history of theology, Adolf von Harnack advanced the thesis
that dogma was "the result of the Hellenization of
Christianity." This means that it was reinterpreted in the
light and on the basis of the categories of Hellenistic
philosophy.[4] Harnack leaves no doubt that he considers
the process of the Hellenization of Christianity a symptom of degeneration and estrangement from its original
character.

Schweitzer's thesis of the purely eschatological attitude of Jesus and of the collapse of the expectation of the end of time because the Parousia did not materialize caused one of his most important followers, Martin Werner, to give a new answer to the question of the origin of dogma in his work *Die Entstehung des christlichen Dogmas*.[5] He proves that the Hellenistic interpretation of the Christian message and the establishment of a new system of Christian faith had become necessary since the first system, the system of early expectation, had collapsed. Werner's work on the origin of Christian dogma consists of carefully conducted verification of the thesis that the early expectation gradually moved into the background. The old system was abandoned because the various elements of early expectation became more unconvincing all the time. It became urgent for the community to overcome the crisis caused by the fact that the Parousia had not come to pass. Simultaneously, the expectations of salvation must be reinterpreted in such a way that they could be reconciled with the new situation.

Briefly, it can be said that the Church realized that it did not represent the community of the chosen of the last generation who are waiting for the return of their Lord and are ready to leap toward him into the clouds. Instead, it became reconciled to its role as a divine institution on this earth. Werner describes this highly dramatic process of reinterpretation in all points of doctrine. This process ended with the final definition of early church dogma at the great ecumenical synods of the fourth to the seventh centuries, where the Church gave permanent form to its dogmas, its constitution, its liturgical order and its canonical writings.

For the original, eschatological doctrine, hope for the future is the solution of all enigmas of this world.

There are no scores of the past which will not be settled finally through salvation at the end of time, which will soon be reached. But hope for the future loses the intensity it had drawn from the expectation of an early advent of the end of time, as established in the original dogma. The problems of present existence, therefore, loom large and again become the old enigmas of this world. Attempts are being made to solve them not by looking into the future, but rather by looking into the past, by trying to explore their origin. There is still a doctrine of the last things. But, as the early expectation of the Kingdom fades away, this doctrine itself becomes a dogmatic problem and is drawn into the process of dogmatic transformation. Its topical value declines and it certainly cannot achieve more than it could originally.[6]

The dogma thus appears as a product of "de-eschatologization"—a rather hideous technical term which is supposed to describe the removal of the original basic attitude toward the end of time in the gospel message. When expressing his ideas about the abandonment of the original early expectation of the Kingdom and its replacement by a Hellenization of the gospel message, Werner draws a picture which is more precise than the term "de-eschatologization."

That eschatology is no longer part of the *early expectation* is a distinction of considerable moment. For the faithful of the apostolic age, eschatology was a mountain. They marched through its crevices and looked for the road to the summit. The faithful of the post-apostolic age have to abandon the bold project. They withdraw and settle in the spacious plains. For them, the mountain of eschatology is on the horizon. Again and again they look longingly toward those heights. But in the hazy distance the mountain can only be seen as a general outline. Details become indistinct and disappear almost entirely.[7]

Although this argument sounds convincing, Werner's framework is not acceptable in this form. The fact that the Parousia did not come, the delay in the coming of the Kingdom, for which everybody had hoped and prayed so intensely, were certainly of decisive importance for the religious life and practical attitudes of early Christianity. However, it is not correct to say that the original framework of faith collapsed within a short time and had to be replaced, in the next phase, by a new one. Rather, the change came very slowly, probably even without being noticed by most people, because a purely eschatological orientation of the Church never existed, that is, it was never completely determined by an early expectation of the Kingdom.

Jesus himself was deeply convinced that the coming Kingdom had arrived with him, that through him the power of the Kingdom of God was already at work, radiating from his person, giving life and performing miracles. With him the Kingdom "in our midst" had begun. From the beginning, the Christian expectation of the end of time had two foci like an ellipse. One focus was the joyous conviction that the Kingdom had arrived, that the time of fulfillment had begun. The other focus was the belief that the time of complete fulfillment was imminent. In the early Church, a development occurred by which, imperceptibly, the point of gravity shifted from an expectation of imminent fulfillment to a consciousness of present salvation.

In this process, the interpretation of Christian doctrine in the light of mysticism and introversion plays an important role indeed. But the second framework did not have to be constructed as an entirely new and strange intellectual model after the collapse of the first one. The roots of the second are already within the first. The only difference is the shift in emphasis from the future to the present. Certain elements of the early expectation disappear or are relegated to a secondary position. Other elements which stress the presence of the Kingdom—as, for example, in the development of the Eucharistic mystery-drama—receive stronger emphasis.

It is not possible, in this context, even to indicate the various phases through which the expectation of an early coming of the Kingdom gradually receded. Great theologians of later periods in the history of the early Church, like Origen, also consider the spiritual interpretation of the firm expectation of the end of time as the decisive point. The image of a returning Jesus, appearing at the end of time on the clouds of heaven, was too palpable for his spiritualism. He changed it into a coming of the Lord into the soul of the faithful. This coming is mediated by the "cloud" of witnesses, namely, the prophets and apostles who speak through the Canon of Holy Scripture.[9]

It cannot be overlooked, however, that, with the fading-out of the idea of the early advent of the Kingdom and the necessity of orienting and establishing the Church in this world, a number of completely new problems arose in the Church. Such problems were not foreseen in the earlier framework. Solutions also had to be found for which this framework had no ready-made answers, and, in order to find them, a bold reinterpretation of canonical texts was necessary.

Instead of describing the process of reinterpretation, we will only set forth its result. We find it in the work of the theologian Augustine, whose thinking on the Kingdom of God has influenced the entire development of the history of the Western Church, not only by forming the idea of the Roman Catholic Church, but also by determining its antithesis, the great Reformation of Luther and Calvin.

Augustine[9] replaced the early expectation of the end of time by an ecclesiastical positivism which equates the visible Catholic Church with the Kingdom of God. The visible Catholic Church, built upon an episcopal constitution, is the true mediator of redemption. Salvation comes only to those who belong to it. This concept was already prepared by earlier fathers of the Church, such as Irenaeus of Lyons and Cyprian of Carthage. But Augustine proclaimed it with greatest emphasis and it gained acceptance because of his authority.

From a historical point of view, it can be said that Augustine represented the final development in which the original expectation of the imminent return of Christ was replaced by the doctrine of the institutional Church as the present Kingdom of God. This development occurred because the events expected for the end of time did not materialize. This replacement of the expectation of the Kingdom of God in the early Church by the doctrine of the Church is one of the most important phases of the process which Martin Werner in his history of dogma calls "de-eschatologization." He considers it one of the most decisive causes for the formation of dogmas.

Time and again Augustine expressed this reinterpretation of the original expectation of the end of time. This is shown very clearly in his concept of the first and second resurrection. The *first resurrection* is not connected any more with the coming of the Last Judgment at the end of time, but rather with the Church. It is the revival of the spirits who were condemned to hell and death. By their faith in the Gospel of the Church, they are revived to a life of bliss. In other words, it affects the spirit and is consummated in baptism. The *second resurrection* affects the body and is accomplished at the end of time when Christ returns for the Last Judgment.

Of equal importance is his reinterpretation of the doctrine of the Millennium. Originally, the community expected the early advent of a blissful end of time in which the chosen would reign together with the Master, after his return, for a period of one thousand years. In his *City of God*, Augustine did not consider the Millennium a kingdom of the future at the end of time. For him it is rather a period in the history of the institutional Church of our time, but he does not commit himself on the actual length of this period.

According to Augustine, even the chaining of Satan is not an eschatological but a historical event. Jesus has already chained Satan—this, in Augustine's opinion, proves the historical success of the Christian Church. Any nation which has entered the sphere of the Christian Church in the past, present, or future is already saved from the power of Satan. While he can still lead individual persons astray, he cannot do so with entire nations. The salvation of nations is realized by the visible Church.

Through Augustine, the gradual disappearance of the early expectation becomes clearly visible. To the extent to which the coming of the Kingdom is increasingly delayed, the idea of the advance-effect of the Kingdom on history becomes ever more powerful. It becomes linked with the proposition that the divine powers of the future Kingdom manifest themselves through the Church here and now. The expectation of the coming of the Kingdom is replaced by the faith that the Kingdom of God is already present in the institution of the Church.

In Augustine, we still find this peculiar connection of his concept of the Church with the expectation of the coming Kingdom in all its glory. But he emphasizes more strongly than did his predecessors that the visible Church is the present pledge of salvation. Within an age doomed to perdition, it is an area of life in which future redemption is already at work.

Augustine drew this conclusion from his ecclesiastical positivism: "Outside the Church there is no salvation—*Extra ecclesiam nulla salus.*"[10] The faith that the visible Church was necessary for salvation already existed before Augustine. Cyprian had expressed this—and his thought was taken over by Augustine and all Catholic theology—in the sentence: *Salus extra ecclesiam non est.* Contrary to the followers of Novatian, Cyprian had already understood the Church as the visible Catholic Church, ruled by bishops in apostolic succession. The Donatists had given their own interpretation to this sentence and believed that, to be the chaste Bride of Christ, the Church had to stand aloof from all bad elements.

As he rejected the doctrine of the Donatists, Augustine was compelled to give a new foundation to the idea that the Church was necessary for salvation. The sentence *Extra ecclesiam nulla salus* means, first of all, that an unbaptized pagan or Jew cannot be a limb of the body of Christ and therefore cannot achieve redemption. But how about heretics and schismatics? It cannot be denied that there are many passages in Augustine's works where he strongly denies that heretics and schismatics could belong to the invisible Church and be saved. The Holy Ghost, he says, is the soul of the Church. This soul only gives life to those limbs which are in the body. If a limb is separated from the body, life does not follow it.[11] Even if a schismatic leads an exemplary life, the crime of schism or heresy still separates him from the Spirit. "The Catholic Church alone is the body of Christ. Its head is the redeemer of the body. The Holy Ghost does not give life to anyone who is not part of this body . . . Therefore the Holy Ghost is not with those who are outside the Church."[12]

Equally significant is Augustine's remark that salvation is only possible in the one ark, namely, the visible Catholic Church. While not everybody in this ark will be saved, those who are outside it will certainly perish. "A man can have a church office, he can have the sacraments, sing the Hallelujah, respond with Amen, adhere to the Gospel, believe in and preach the name of the Father, the Son, and the Holy Ghost, but nowhere except in the Catholic Church will he find salvation."[13] There is no doubt that, for Augustine, those who are sanctified "must be assembled and thrashed on the thrashing-floor of the Catholic Church." Within the Church, there can be good and bad, grain and chaff. But, outside it, only the bad exist.[14]

This is the point at which the reinterpretation of the expectation of the end of time into the doctrine of the institutional Church emerges with greatest clarity. The institution, which represents the Kingdom of God on earth, wants to protect and expand its power with the means which this power puts at its disposal. He was convinced that salvation could only be found in the institutions of the Church. Since he also had the strong desire to lead all heretics and schismatics back to the Church, as the only place of salvation, Augustine finally even allowed the defense of the forcible return of the Donatists into the Church.

Augustine has indeed become the protagonist of the *Cogite intrare*. His attitude on the question of the use of the power of the State in matters of church discipline has been investigated repeatedly. This attitude was subject to several rather noticeable changes. In the beginning, he rejected any interference of the State in religious controversies and especially any application of force against schismatics. He believed that a convincing presentation of the truth and friendly persuasion could do away with schism. Thus he himself tried to bring about a conciliation of the opposing groups by sermons, letters of exhortation, and by suggesting that conferences be held in common.

But when the Donatists, and particularly their allies,

the Circumcellions, used force and, finally, open rebellion, he was led to approve more vigorous fighting methods. He wondered whether a forcible suppression of the schism by imperial decree would not be more appropriate. In his work *Contra epistolam Parmeniani* (circa A.D. 400), Augustine defended the right of the Emperor to enact laws dealing with religion. Since the Emperor may take action against paganism, he is also entitled to take measures against a Christian sect, particularly if it uses force and rebellion as was the case with the Donatists.

The most explicit defense of imperial legislation on religion and, at the same time, a detailed explanation of the change in his own mind are given by Augustine in his *Epistle* 93 to Vincentius (A.D. 408). Here he refers to that passage of Holy Scripture which he will quote so frequently in the future: *Cogite intrare* (Compel them to come in—Luke 14:23). Still, Augustine remained firmly opposed to the death penalty. He demanded that the punishment of heretics and schismatics be humane and meted out in kindness and love.[15] But in the light of his institutional interpretation of the Church, it can no longer be denied that a church institution that uses the means of the secular State to enforce its own claims to power is well on the way to becoming a worldly power itself.

Another mark of Augustine's ecclesiastical positivism is the fact that, in analogy to the sacrament of baptism, he considered priestly ordination as a sacrament. He thus created the doctrine of the indestructible character—*character indelebilis*—which the sacrament bestows upon the ordained person. Ordination engraves a sign of mysterious power on the ordained. It cannot be wiped off. Just as there is a mark on soldiers, so there is a mark of ordination. Just as the soldier can be recognized, without fail, by the mark, even if he is a deserter, so the ordained priest keeps the mark which was impressed upon him by ordination. An ordained Catholic priest can never again become a layman. He can never divest himself of the unique power of the priesthood. A stamp has been impressed upon him which no power in heaven or on earth can ever wipe off. The authority bestowed upon him by ordination keeps its power and efficacy regardless of the personal ethical qualities of the ordained man. It is even independent of his intellectual and religious development. If an ordained Catholic priest defects to heresy, his priestly authority, his "character" is not destroyed. If he is received back in the Church, he does not have to be ordained again.[16]

This doctrine of the *sacramentum ordinis*—the sacrament of priestly ordination—means that the principle of a profound distinction between priest and layman becomes firmly established in the Catholic Church. The place of the charismatic person in the community of the end of time is taken by the ordained priest. He is a person who is set apart from all other Christians by a peculiar, supernatural, spiritual qualification for his office which is independent of his personal qualities.

It is another significant facet of this positivism that Augustine has brought about a clarification of the relationship between Scripture and authority within the Church. The institutional Church needs not only the spiritually and legally valid ministry, but also the spiritually and legally valid norm of Holy Scripture.

For Augustine, the word of Holy Scripture is the highest, all-surpassing authority. It is the Word of God in a very distinct sense, Christianity's manifest document of redemption, a letter from home to the citizens of the Kingdom of God during their pilgrimage on earth, a nonrecallable bill of exchange, by which God has undertaken obligations to man and which remains unchanged through generations. In fact, Scripture itself is the presence of Christ.[17]

Because of its divine origin, Scripture cannot contain either error or lie: *Sancta Scriptura fallere non potest*— Holy Scripture cannot err.[18] Its authority stands high above any other. Compared to it, even decisions of church councils appear to be human documents. Any special opinion, even if it comes from a pious, yet fallible bishop, any practices of an individual church which are contrary to Scripture, must yield to its clear text. Only Scripture is entirely pure and infallible, while errors turn up even in the best work of man. Scripture alone is the measure of truth. During his last years, Augustine used it to measure his entire life's work and revoked in his *Retractationes* all the false interpretations of Holy Scripture to be found in his earlier writings.

Augustine's emphatic expressions on the unique significance of Holy Scripture were destined, in particular, to find their highest recognition among the reformers of the sixteenth century. But, for him, Scripture is never isolated from the Church. In fact, Augustine knows of a variety of relationships between the Church and Scripture. Because of its age, the Church is the only guarantee that the scriptural heritage will be passed on to posterity faithfully. But it also determines, by right of ownership, which books belong to it and which do not. This means that it decides whether a book is part of the canon or not. The Church is also indispensable for the interpretation of the various books of Scripture which are part of the canon.

In the last analysis, Augustine does not see the rule of faith—*regula fidei*—in the written word, but rather in the living, conscious faith of the Church. He never expressed the thought, which is quite common in the Eastern Church, that the Church itself created Scripture, nor did he ever point to the fact that the Church had existed for a considerable period of time without the New Testament canon. Yet, for him, the most important principle of interpretation is that Scripture cannot contradict the faith of the Church and that, therefore, under all circumstances, it has to be interpreted in the light of the faith of the Church.

The last step on the road to the abandonment of the old end-of-time character of the Church can be seen in the fact that the bishop, as the holder of the *Cathedra Christi*—the Chair of Christ—becomes the true focus of the Church's faith. As bearer of the truth and holder of the teaching office in the Church he has the duty to defend the Church's truth against the false doctrines of the heretics. In this connection, it becomes particularly important to note that in the bishops the apostles are present, and Christ, in turn, is speaking through them.[19] Instead of a future return of the exalted Lord, the founder of the Church is brought into the present by a continuous succession of officeholders whom he himself has appointed. The expectation of the end of time looks to the future; the consciousness of office looks to the past. Since the Catholic Church is the *Cathedra Christi,* Christ himself speaks to humanity through the man who occupies the Chair, the bishop. If the bishop, therefore, speaks to the people, he does so in the name of Christ, the Bishop of all bishops. Sometimes the word of the shepherd is more important for the flock than the particular passage of the Scripture which he interprets. Thus Augustine can say to those who have just been baptized: *Ecce codices vestri nos sumus*—I am your Bible.[20]

The bishop holds this teaching position because of his office and not because of his personal sanctity. The truth is tied to the Chair and not to the person of the bishop. As the sacraments are valid, even if the priest who gave them is morally unworthy, so also the voice of truth speaks through the bishop, even if he is not very good. His preaching manifests clearly that Christ is behind every proclamation of the Church. If the holder of the Chair is unworthy, this does not lower the *Cathedra veritatis* to a *Cathedra pestilentiae*.[21]

In his magnificent apology of the Christian Church, the twenty-two books of the *City of God*, Augustine took it for granted that the Church represented the heavenly Kingdom of God on earth. It did not occur to him to follow the Byzantine ideology of the Kingdom and to oppose the Christian empire of Byzantium to the Ostrogothic, pagan kingdom of Rome, which persecutes the martyrs and kills the saints. For Augustine, the great antagonist of the pagan world empire in the history of salvation is not the Christian empire of Constantinople. The myth of the apocalyptic vision of the harlot on the seven hills is not set against the Christian myth of Byzantium as the New Rome, but against the world power of the Catholic Church.

It is not surprising that Augustine's concept of the Church was used to justify the church-state idea. It is not surprising, either, that his concept of the Church was the germ for the idea of papal primacy. For Augustine himself, this idea did not play a significant role. It was activated in Roman church politics a few generations later.

With Augustine, the gradual abandonment of the original early expectation of the Kingdom of God by the early Church has come to its conclusion. The Church has become a powerful, supranational institution, a guardian of the sacraments entrusted to it, and a historical manifestation of the heavenly Kingdom. Christ has established its apostolic order, and invested it with both spiritual and temporal power. It has thus taken the place of the future Kingdom of God itself. Previous ideas of the last things, which had been considered palpable realities in the early Church, have been relegated to a final chapter of church dogmatics. They are devaluated to a doctrine of the last things, which cannot have any alarming, threatening or even revolutionary effect. There is no fear that they will hasten the downfall of all temporal things.

III

The Expectation of the End of Time and the Doctrine of Evolution in the Middle Ages

Despite the victory of the idea of the church institution, the early expectation of the end of time emerged repeatedly in medieval church history. Particularly around the year A.D. 1000, wide circles in the Church were seized by the expectation of an early end, of the return of Christ, and the imminent establishment of the Kingdom of God.

The development of medieval sects is also connected with the awakening of a new expectation of the imminent end of time. But it is not our intention to deal here with this particular problem. We would rather deal with another, completely new type of Christian expectation of the end of time in which the idea of evolution and progress is applied for the first time to the history of salvation: the doctrine of the three ages by the prophetic abbot Joachim of Fiore.[1]

Joachimitism is not as new as it may appear. As we emphasized in the first chapter, Montanism already knew the element of progress in the history of salvation. It was brought about by the Paraclete, whose coming leads to the age of redemption by the Holy Ghost. The doctrine of the Holy Ghost, as evolved in Montanism, found its spontaneous development in Joachim of Fiore (circa 1132–1202), the prophetic abbot and founder of the monastery of San Giovanni in Fiore, a village on the heights of the wild Sila Mountains in Calabria.[2] The concept of the Holy Ghost as a creative power initiating a new phase of the history of salvation was again spontaneously brought to the fore by him. He took a critical attitude toward the institutional, universal Church of the present time.

Joachim's doctrine of the Spirit became the basis for one of the greatest spiritual revolutions of the Middle Ages. Those circles of reformers who, in the thirteenth and fourteenth centuries, adopted his teachings of the coming "status" of the Holy Spirit became the protagonists of the revolution through which ecclesiastical feudalism in the Middle Ages was overcome. This doctrine also was the starting point for many social and political ideas of modern times. There is a direct connection between Joachimite Spiritualism and the criticism which radical Franciscans directed against the ideological basis of the medieval papacy. Up to the sixteenth century it also influenced the beginnings of most of the reforming and revolutionary movements.[3]

Abbot Joachim developed his new concept of the course of the history of salvation on the basis of his own personal experience of the Holy Spirit. On the morning of Pentecost 1190, he had an illumination while studying the book of Revelation. "At the time of Matins, I woke up and took that book to meditate . . . Suddenly the brightness of knowledge came to the eyes of my spirit. The fulfillment of the book was revealed to me and the inner harmony—*concordia*—which exists between the Old and the New Testament."[4]

For Joachim, this pentecostal illumination was the conclusion of decades of indefatigable effort to understand the complete cause of the history of salvation. He considered it a liberating and redeeming inspiration which gave him, in a flash, an understanding of the inner relations within the divine system of salvation. His basic insight is that the order of the history of salvation and the course of its completion are connected with the threefold nature of God. The divine Trinity determines the form in which redemption will be achieved inasmuch as a special period of salvation and a special world age correspond to each of the three persons of the Holy Trinity. In each of them, salvation manifests itself and is realized in a special way.

The Trinity manifests itself progressively in three successive periods of the history of salvation. Each of these periods is dedicated to one of the divine persons, and its peculiar nature—*proprietas*—corresponds to the nature of the particular person of the Trinity. The first period of salvation is the age of the Father; the second, that of the Son; and the third, that of the Holy Ghost.

The principle of development and progress is thus applied to the observation of history. Development and progress are not understood in human terms, as the growth of a germ which has been planted within humanity itself. They are, rather, considered as steps in the progressive self-realization and self-revelation of the divine Trinity in the history of mankind. In the actual course and consummation of the history of salvation, this intervention has the effect of a clearly discernible progress directed toward a distinct goal. The age of the Holy Spirit will bring the concluding revelation and the abundance of salvation itself.

The definition of the limits of the periods of salvation is the second facet of Joachim's enlightenment. It is the revelation of the inner connection existing between the past two periods of salvation and the Old and the New Testaments. The future course and progress of the history of salvation can be deduced from the course and relationship of the two previous ones. The correct typological interpretation of the characters and events of the two Testaments and the establishment of the correct relationship between them reveal a surprising inner harmony. Each character of the Old Testament gives the direction, pattern, and promise of a character or community of salvation which emerge in the second period of redemption, that of the New Testament. Those two periods correspond in every respect. All persons, groups, and events are parallel not only by their chronological order, but also by the connection of their inner significance.

Joachim became a prophet because of this elucidation of the inner relationship which exists between the first two periods of the history of salvation, those of the Old and New Testaments. How salvation will be realized in the future, third period can be predicted from the manner in which it came to pass in the first two, those of the Father and of the Son. The development of the history of salvation goes on, but it is based on a scheme of inner harmony.

The decisive passage in which Joachim elaborates his doctrine of a successive realization of the divine Trinity in the sequence of three periods of salvation is the following:[5]

> The secrets of the Holy Scripture direct us to three systems of the universe: The first one, in which we lived under the Law; the second one, in which we lived under grace; and the third one, which we expect soon, in which even more abundant grace will be granted to us. For, as John says, God will give us grace for grace, faith in return for love, and both of them in equal measure.
>
> Thus, in the first period learning prevails, in the second one partly completed wisdom, but in the third one the fullness of knowledge.
>
> The first one has the servitude of slaves, the second one the servitude of sons, the third one will bring freedom.
>
> The first one is one of fear, the second one of faith, the third one of love.

The first is the period of servants, the second one of free men, the third one of friends.

The first is the period of boys, the second one of men, the third one of old men.

The first one is lit by the stars, the second one by the light of dawn, the third one by the brightness of day.

The first one belongs to winter, the second one to the first days of spring, the third one to summer.

The first one brings forth primroses, the second one roses, the third one lilies.

The first one brings forth grass, the second one stems, the third one ears of corn.

The first one brings water, the second one wine, the third one oil.

The first period relates to the Father, the second one to the Son, the third one to the Holy Ghost.

What these images have in common is that they show the sequence of periods of salvation as a continuous progression. The Holy Ghost is the force in history which brings about and directs this progress in the history of salvation. Joachim is the first theologian of history who introduced the idea of progress into the theology of history. The frequent use of this term is supported by a typological exegesis of Luke 2:52: "And Jesus increased in wisdom and in stature, and in favor with God and man." According to Joachim's typological method of interpretation, Jesus represents the Church. The progress made by the child Jesus, according to the Gospel of Luke, refers to the progress of the Church. It passes first through the periods of the Father and of the Son, and then aims toward the period of the Holy Ghost in which it will find its highest degree, its fullness.[6]

The spiritual order—*ordo spiritualis*—which will lead the Church from the second to the third period "will progress from day to day, as in different stages of growth, in an effort to please God as diligently as possible and to serve men with all its strength." The "progress of the world" therefore has the aim to realize and bring to maturity the last and perfect period. "Men of the spirit" whose influence Joachim already sees at work in his own period will prevail in it.[7] Under their guidance, the Church will progress, through the gift of the Holy Spirit, "toward a chosen generation and a royal priesthood" (I Peter 2:9).

What is decisively new in this doctrine of the three ages of the universe is that it is being applied to the concrete course of world history. On the basis of a computation of figures and generations which we do not want to repeat here in detail,[8] Joachim comes to the conclusion that the beginning of the age of the Holy Ghost must be expected for the year A.D. 1260.

This commitment on the beginning of the third period has extraordinary consequences for Joachim's outlook on his own time. The idea implies nothing less than the announcement that the time of the Christian Church, in the institutional form that it had until now, will end soon. A new form of the Church, the Church of the Spirit, will emerge in the near future.

The age of the Holy Ghost, the emergence of which Joachim foresees, is an age of creative transformation for the Church. This transformation extends to all areas of church life. It does not only relate to spiritual perceptions by Christians, but also to the institution of the Church as it has existed until now. It also affects the entire sacramental life of the Church, and even the old method of transmission of divine revelation through Holy Scripture. The previous form of ecclesiastical ethics is also subjected to a thorough transformation. As a matter of course, the old social structure of the Church is transformed as well.

It takes a total view of all these various elements to get

the entire picture of the time of the Spirit, as conceived by Joachim, and of the revolutionary consequences of his theology of the Spirit. In this picture, the history of salvation appears, first of all, as a history of the progressive enlightenment of mankind through the medium of an ever-increasing knowledge of salvation. The creative action of the Holy Ghost, who is the moving force in the history of salvation, has as its aim to bring about the breakthrough of the *intelligentia spiritualis* which will emerge in its pure form during the third period of salvation.

The progress of the understanding of salvation is therefore not identical with the development of human reason in the world. There is a transcendental influence at work which brings about progressive enlightenment and uses methods which are germane to each age of salvation.

Thus, in the first age, the understanding of salvation is given through the instrumentality of the Law which communicates to man the positive will of God the Father. The second one brings a deeper understanding because it gives to man the Gospel of Jesus Christ. But this Gospel still does not represent the highest degree of the understanding of salvation. It still shows the divine mysteries wrapped in symbols, images, and sacraments. Only the third age will bring the true spiritual disclosure of the entire divine truth.

In the third period, that in which the faithful are enlightened by the full daylight of the Holy Ghost, the Spirit works as the pure principle of inwardness. "For he does not dwell in material things that are made by hand, but in the lap of inner man, so that, by comparing spiritual matters, he can show man all the abundance of truth."[9] It is a consequence of this idea that the validity of Holy Scripture and of the sacraments is restricted to the second period of salvation. It loses its significance in the third period, when it will be replaced by the higher

understanding of salvation through the *intelligentia spiritualis.*

Joachim has expressed this revolutionary thought un-
mistakably. The letter of Holy Scripture in the second
period compares with spiritual understanding in the third
period as baptism by water compares to baptism by fire.
In this connection, Joachim can actually refer to the abolition and destruction of the letter of Holy Scripture. The
fire of the Holy Ghost which falls down from the third
heaven will bring a spiritual understanding "which will
remove and consume that temporal surface of the letter
which is made of earth and speaks of earth so that the
imperfect will be removed at the arrival of the perfect."[10]

There is an even more important chain of developments. Joachim calls the first period one of the servitude
of slaves, the second one the period of the sons, the third
one the period of freedom. This thought had a particularly revolutionary effect, because here the history of
salvation was understood as the process of gradual realization of the freedom of the Holy Spirit. It is not surprising that, at an early stage, this idea not only pointed the
way to church revolution but also had social-revolutionary
effects. The point of departure for Joachim is found in
Paul's second letter to the Corinthians: "Where the Spirit
of the Lord is, there is freedom" (3:17).

God did not give man the full freedom of the Spirit
from the very beginning. It is only reached as the last
stage in a long process of the history of salvation. The
kingdom of freedom is indeed the real goal of the history
of salvation, which appears to be the progressive realization of God-given freedom.

In the first age, that of the Father, humanity is still under the discipline of the Law, which treats men as "servants of God." The second period, that of the Son, already
brings a greater measure of freedom inasmuch as, through
Christ, men have been raised to the status of children of

God. But, as children of God, they are still subject to the direct discipline of the Father. This is why the second period is called that of the "servitude of sons." It is the third phase in which the sons, who have been prepared by Christ, will reach the state of complete freedom. "For you were called to freedom" (Gal. 5:13), which is given as a promise to the Church of the New Testament, will not be fully realized till the third period.[11]

In this connection Joachim also mentions the motif of "God's friendship." God's friendship is the goal of the development in the relationship between God and man. It is more than the state of children of God. It is the last, highest, and concluding form that the relationship between God and man takes. Only the third age of salvation is that of the "Friends of God." For the understanding of the movement of the Friends of God in the fourteenth century,[12] it is important to know that the term "friend of God" has eschatological connotations. Only in the period of salvation of the Holy Ghost will it be possible for the faithful to be elevated to the rank of friend of God which is equivalent to the state of freedom.

Materially, Joachim defines this freedom as freedom of love,[13] that is, freedom of man's complete and voluntary devotion to God and to his fellowman. In this state, man returns his freedom to God. Satan and, under Satan's influence, Adam took their decision against the will of God. This possibility has been overcome now, since the Holy Ghost has awakened love in the hearts of men.

The idea of a progressive development of the history of salvation is expressed most noticeably when we look at the sequence of the ethical and social forms of the various periods of salvation. Joachim's basically radical and ascetic character and point of view are shown here most poignantly. The age of the Holy Ghost brings fulfillment of the most radical postulates of spiritual sanctity and perfection.

Thus the history of salvation becomes a history of the education of humanity in which the Spirit is the creative, pedagogical principle. The first age, that of the Father, makes certain concessions to the carnal nature of man. While man is expected to observe the divine ethical laws, certain mitigations, such as legal polygamy, are still allowed.

The second period has an intermediate character inasmuch as the concession of polygamy, granted to the faithful, is abolished. Those who belong to the Church must practice monogamy. Besides this new Christian concept of marriage, different and more radical forms of asceticism begin to take shape. The Church of the second period is represented by the clergy who lead the celibate life. Since the beginning of the Christian Church, monks, in their various orders, have appeared side by side with the clergy. They anticipated the order of the *viri spirituales* of the age of the Spirit. The progress of life in meditation proceeds apace with the progress of the ascetic postulates of sanctification.

The third age is the time of the *vita contemplativa*, the complete dedication to spiritual understanding. It is identical with divine spiritual service, the "worship of God in spirit and in truth," and with the pure implementation of Christian love.[14]

Besides the pattern of gradual progress, there is that of the division and sharp contrast of the ages. Although the Church of the third period appears to be the final result of a gradual development, having regard to its models in the second period, Joachim can still describe it as a new creation, which replaces the decaying and degenerate period of the clerical Church. In many passages of his writings, Joachim ruthlessly criticizes the shortcomings of the institutional Church of the second period and believes that it is in a state of disintegration. Compared to this degenerate Church of the expiring age, the coming one of the contemplative Church, which he initiated himself, will be the New Jerusalem and a completely new creation. Reformation becomes revolution.

Yet, the patterns of progress and new creation are not mutually exclusive. Each age experiences the gradual disintegration of its existing social patterns and forms of understanding—they will be overcome by new creations at the beginning of the next age. But the new patterns and forms which will emerge from those new creations have a relationship of inner continuity with the previous ones. They are the fulfillment of the prototypes of the previous age which have pointed the way to the future.

The ideal of the spiritual man of the third age has overtones of the old Montanist ideal of the superman. The idea of restoration, suggesting that the beginning will be restored in the end, cannot find a place in Joachim's framework of progressive history. By the constantly renewed influence of the Holy Ghost, humanity will be raised to an ever higher level. The last stage, which will be reached in the spiritual order of the third age, is a transformation from human to superhuman or angelic life.

Thus Joachim characterizes progress in relation to the various types of spiritual life found in the different periods by this sequence: fathers—sons—angelic spirits (*patres—filii—angelici spiritus*). The fathers signify the period of the Old Testament. The sons are those Christians whom Christ has raised to that state—they represent the stage of the New Testament. The *angelici spiritus* are the members of the contemplative order which was formed "in the image of the Holy Ghost." The charismatic person who is filled with the Spirit has spiritual understanding and leads the perfect spiritual life. He is already exalted to the superhuman, angelic level.

Joachim changes the Christian expectation of the end of time by expecting a Kingdom of the Holy Ghost as the final form of the Christian Church in history. Thus he touches the basic pillar of the historical and theological self-justification of the Roman Church. For he includes the church institution itself, which is based upon the primacy of Peter, in the process of development of the history of salvation. In view of the coming period of the Spirit, the papal Church is just a passing stage in the development of the history of salvation. According to Joachim, the papacy, in its present form, is restricted to the second age of the universe, the age of the Son.

Within this second age, the papacy represents the proper contemporary form of the ecclesiastical community. This, however, implies that, in the third age, the papacy will not "fit in" any more. The papacy will no longer exist in its present form. Joachim does not only speak of a dissolution of the church institution in the second period, but actually of its death. As John the evangelist succeeds Peter, the order of the future *viri spirituales* will succeed the bishops. This succession of the orders of salvation presupposes the end of the group which will be succeeded. "As Peter dies the death of a martyr, John survives him for a long time. Thus the papal Church, which has Peter as its historical prototype, dies. The Church of the Spirit—the Church of John—will survive to the end of the world. It will succeed the pope of Rome up to the ocean and from the river to the limits of the earth."[15]

Joachim thus became the creator of the expectation of "Johannine Christianity" as the last and highest form of Christianity in the history of salvation. It was destined to have a far-reaching effect on the Christian theology of history, and dominated many spirits up to the period of German romanticism, as represented by Franz von Baader, Fichte, Hegel, and Schelling. Its aftereffects can still be found in Russian religious philosophy up to Soloviev and Berdyaev.[16]

To summarize: Joachim considered the historical efficacy of the Holy Ghost from a dual point of view—one, of continuous development and progress; the other, from the viewpoint of new creation. The main historical and theological categories of the first standpoint are *proficere, ascendere, progressio, mutatio, processus, successio*. The main historico-typological categories of the second point of view are *consummatio, renovatio, reformatio, recreatio, resurrectio*.

Proceeding from there, the history of salvation is considered, on the one hand, as a continuous process which is moving, step by step, in all areas of life. This applies to understanding as well as to social reforms and ethics, to the postulate of sanctity as well as to the religious relationship between man and God. On the other hand, this same historical process is understood as a succession of new creations and new births. The old categories of the individual times of salvation are used up and perish. They are consumed and replaced.

It appears that the two viewpoints of constant development and continuous re-creation are mutually exclusive. In actual fact, they are dialectically interdependent. Their connection represents the secret of historical life itself. All development, all progress, is a dramatic process of continuous death and continuous rebirth. "If Almighty God wants to terminate—*consummare*—the old to create the new, he allows persecution to arise within the Church. Then he abandons what he wants to terminate and protects that which he wants to live on. Thus we can say that the new and the good, which were hidden in the dark, can be brought to light when the opportunity arises."[17]

In a unique way, Joachim thus understands that the Holy Ghost is the effective force in the history of salvation, which leads God's plan of redemption to its completion by steadily progressing new creation.

By joining the ideas of progress and development with the prophecy of the imminent fulfillment of the history of salvation, Joachim has created the model for the religious, social, political, and philosophical utopias of modern times. In his own works, the image of the coming third period is still completely determined by the evangelical postulates of sanctity. But when he describes the community organization of the third age, he outlines certain social-utopian ideas. These emerge most clearly among the radical Spiritual Franciscans in their fight for an uncompromising realization of the Franciscan ideal of poverty. Significantly enough, the social-utopian elements of Joachimitism are particularly noticeable among the Hussites of Bohemia and among those in Germany who were influenced by them as well as in the Joachimitism of the time of the Reformation.

But all this does not remain a utopia. There is the prophetic consciousness that the new, the future age, is secretly at work and that it will soon come to life in all its fullness. This gives a revolutionary impulse to the Joachimite way of looking at history.

Joachim did not merely consider himself a prophet, but also a trailblazer of the coming time of salvation. His purpose in founding the Order was to help realize the promised *ordo spiritualis* of the end of time. But he was not a conscious revolutionary himself. Nevertheless, his theology of the Spirit forced the prophet, with a certain inner logic, to contribute actively toward the overcoming of the present age and to help in bringing about the coming of the promised one. It is that promise of the imminent coming of the age of fulfillment which beckons to the man of the present so that he may be ready for the imminent transformation, indeed, to anticipate the future by preparing the transformation himself. Here the Holy Ghost becomes the active ferment in the transformation of life and of society as a whole.

IV

The Expectation of the End of Time and Revolution

Joachim of Fiore and his doctrine of the coming Kingdom of the Holy Spirit has led us to the subject of the Christian expectation of the end of time and revolution.

In our image of the modern world, the Christian Church represents a factor of political and social conservatism, opposing the violent overthrow of existing social conditions by revolution. But this is only true in regard to institutionalized Christianity, whether it be an independent or a state church, in which the radical eschatological impulses have been tamed. At all times, however, impulses of reformation and even revolution have issued from Christian communities which were dominated by a newly awakened expectation of the early coming of the Kingdom of God.[1]

The transition from reformation to revolution can be established very precisely. It comes when the followers of such radical groups, who hope that the end of time and the Kingdom of God are imminent, cease to expect or to "wait patiently" for the Kingdom. Instead, they begin to hasten its coming, even by force, and try to anticipate the Kingdom of God by their own revolutionary action. They jump from idea to revolutionary action. A significant example of this process is the transition of leftist Hegelians, particularly of Karl Marx, from their teacher's philosophy of history to political revolution.[2]

Even the Gospel of Matthew speaks of people who "want to establish the Kingdom of Heaven by force."

They are described as *biastai*, the violent ones (Mt. 11:12). Such violent ones who cannot or will not wait for the coming of fulfillment, but wish to gain the Kingdom of Heaven by force, have existed in all critical periods of church history. They were also the secret impulses of all European revolutions.

In all periods, we notice a certain structural similarity among these eschatological revolutionaries. It makes no difference whether they are sectarian revolutionaries of medieval church history, or of the Reformation or English Revolution, whether they belong to radical North American sects or to chiliastic, social-revolutionary movements of modern Africa.

The revolutionary transformation of Christian expectations is well illustrated by Thomas Münzer,[3] the leader of the radical wing of the German Reformation, whose open rebellion could not be crushed until all the princes of Central Germany who were sympathetic to the Lutheran Reformation took concerted action against him.

An examination of the religious basis of the radical tendencies within the German Reformation also reveals another paradox, namely, that Christian mysticism is the root of the piety of such unruly spirits as Carlstadt, the Zwickau prophets, and Thomas Münzer. The sources of Münzer's spiritual life are particularly Tauler and the *Theologia Deutsch*.[4]

How is it possible that a completely introverted piety can suddenly turn into revolutionary action? For an answer, we have to look at the innermost purpose of mystical piety itself which seeks the immediacy of religious experience. Mysticism looks for the experience of direct union with God. It wants God as he really is, and rejects all expedients interposed between man and God. This includes not only all institutional and liturgical expedients, but in the end, even that form of mediation which considers Holy Scripture as a historical document of divine revelation.

In times in which the life of the Church has become completely institutionalized, many expedients can be established between man and God. Criticism of the Church can then suddenly be converted into the will to break open the road of immediate access to God and to take up the fight, in the name of the Holy Ghost, against a Church which has become immured in its own institutions.

In the golden age of medieval mysticism, particularly in the works of Meister Eckhart, we frequently find the key expression *Deus nudus*, the "naked" God, or Deity *in se*.[5] The mystics want to have God, as he really is, "without modalities," as Meister Eckhart puts it "without images," without his attributes, without his outward manifestations. Meister Eckhart formulated this in an almost blasphemous manner: you have to want God "the way he is in his bathroom,"[6] which means without "clothing," attributes or outward manifestation.

The urge for immediacy, implied in these remarks, can assume revolutionary forms wherever this mysticism becomes popular. It can lead to open revolution, if two conditions are met. First, the ecclesiastical apparatus itself must be considered an obstacle to free access to God. The second condition is widening, popularization, and coarsening of the positions of mysticism. It will be reduced to some kind of mystical primitivism which is not built upon a deeper education of the mind. For emotional reasons and in the name of immediate religious experience it is therefore much more prepared to choose as its program the removal of the institutional apparatus.

This situation was reached in Germany at the beginning of the sixteenth century. We hardly realize nowadays how widespread the discontent about the ruling Church's institutions was at that time. Some storm signals of a revolutionary turn of mysticism had preceded this situation in the fourteenth century: The "Brethren of the Free Spirit" had already largely seceded from the institutional Church, to live up to their postulate of an immediate personal experience of God and of the gifts of the Spirit. However, they did not yet launch an assault against the Church. They merely tried to separate, to the extent to which this was possible under the pressure of the ruling system.[7]

In the meantime, general social discontent had grown too. The social oppression of the peasants, the social indignation of the petty bourgeoisie, the artisans and the semi-burgesses, but particularly the social indignation in the relatively young but rapidly developing mining industry had led to a latent readiness for a revolutionary outbreak. Significantly enough, the transition from mysticism to revolution occurred in the mining districts of Saxony and Thuringia, such as Allstedt, Zwickau, and Mühlhausen. The emotional fuel of a popularized and primitivized mysticism could easily serve as a reinforcement of social discontent. The mystical fire served as the core of the revolutionary flame, the part where the flame is hottest.

The last push for a transition to open revolution was given by the conviction which is the impulse of all radical reformations. Wide circles were deeply convinced that the Church, as it presented itself to the public of its time and with its institution of penance and its sacramental practices, was corrupt at the root. Indeed, the corruption had already seized head and limbs, the Antichrist himself had taken his seat on the supreme Chair of the Church. Nothing can, therefore, be improved in the old Church by a patchwork of reforms, by the old methods. It is this realization which creates the conditions for the decisive step: If nothing can be improved, then let us get rid of the whole thing!

This is the point of departure of the radical Reformation which has been neglected in the German historiography of the Reformation. As recently as 1962, an American published a comprehensive presentation of the radical Reformation which fills the gaps of German research into the history of the Reformation. We refer to the work of George H. Williams, professor at the Harvard Divinity School, *The Radical Reformation*.[8]

It is significant that, in Germany, Thomas Münzer was first discovered by the historiographers of dialectical materialism. He has since remained the favorite of Marxist works on the history of the Church. This trend began when Karl Kautsky, the leader of the German Social Democrats, wrote a book on Münzer[9] in which he described him as a forerunner of socialism and as the great rebel of the Reformation period. Ernst Bloch also devoted a monograph to Münzer and interpreted him further in the spirit of dialectical materialism. In the Eastern Zone, Münzer is nowadays one of the few legitimate subjects a church historian is permitted to handle.

The Marxist interpretation of Münzer is, of course, very biased. Neither his revolutionary activity nor his political and social program can in any way be separated from the mystical basis of his piety. Münzer was born in 1488 at Stolberg, in the Harz Mountains, and received a thorough theological education. He tried hard to get a good universal education and collected a large library. Graduating from Frankfurt on the Oder, he became an assistant cleric at Halle, and then moved to Zwickau where he was drawn into the religious and social problems which dominated that mining town. Silver mining had attracted thousands of miners from Franconia and Thuringia. But the levers of local power were held exclusively by a handful of mine-owners. With all the arrogance of their class, they looked down upon the masters of the guilds, an increasing number of whom had lost their independence. The value of

money dropped and prices rose because of the great silver
production and the conversion of artisans' shops into big
concerns. From a social viewpoint, there was also a revolutionary atmosphere in Zwickau.[10]

By his sermons in Zwickau, Münzer quickly helped to
make conditions even more extreme. He spread the idea
of the total corruption and incorrigibility of existing
church conditions and extended it to the political situation. In the few publications of his which have been preserved, he refers repeatedly to information which he
found in the *Ecclesiastical History* of Eusebius and in
which the following is reported about Hegesippus, an
early Church writer: "Hegesippus, a credible writer of history and pupil of the apostles, says clearly in the fifth
book of the *Explanations*, and so does Eusebius in the
fourth book of the *Christian Church*, that the holy Bride
of Jesus remained a virgin until the immediate pupils of
the apostles died. Afterwards, she became an obscene
adulteress. Such plain history books make it quite clear
what Christianity was like when our fathers adopted that
faith, as long as six hundred years ago."[11]

Early church tradition thus confirms Münzer's worst
suspicion that the decay of the present Church has a long
history. The purity of the Christian Church had only
been of short duration. General corruption set in right
after the death of the pupils of the apostles. The Germans, who adopted Christianity around the turn from
the eighth to the ninth century, did not receive the true
Christian faith, but one that had been degenerating for a
long time. From the beginning, they were raised in a corrupt Christianity.

And now comes Münzer's revolutionary conclusion:
What we need is not a reformed or improved Church. We
need a new Church. This is the decisive word for us:
"God will do wondrous things," or as he says in his
Prague Proclamation of November 1, 1521: "God will do

wondrous things with those he has chosen, particularly in this country. The *New Church* will be established here. This people will be the mirror of the entire world. Therefore I appeal to everybody to help, that the Word of God may be defended. Through the spirit of Elijah, I will show you those who have taught you to bring sacrifices for the idol Baal. If you will not do it, God will let you be slain by the Turks next year. Verily, I know whereof I speak, and that this is so. And therefore I will suffer what Jeremiah had to endure."[12]

Thus he takes the decisive step toward a new beginning. Here we can distinguish the significant difference between the radical Reformation and the conservative Reformation of Luther. Luther did not want to create a new Church. He wanted to cleanse the Catholic Church of its later symptoms of degeneration and re-establish it in its original form. For Münzer, the demand for a New Church is decisive.

From here on, it is merely a question of method. What degree of intensity should be used to make the New Church a reality and to what extent should the New Church be built by first destroying the old one? It is a question which, later on, will also have to be answered by dialectical materialism: Is it still possible to improve the old society by evolution or is it necessary to remove the ruling class in order to introduce the new social order by revolution? Such considerations are later found, on a political level, in the theory and practice of the Bolshevik Revolution. In the context of church history, we find them already in Thomas Münzer.

In the Prague Proclamation of 1521, the demand for a New Church is still made as an ideological program. But two and a half years later, in his letter to the tax-collector Hans Zeyss, dated July 22, 1524, he says: "Whoever wants to be a stone of the New Church, must risk his neck. Otherwise, the builders will throw him away."[13]

"To risk his neck" means that he must stake his life on active participation in the destruction of the old Church. This revolutionary readiness is also directed against present Christian authorities, who protect the false Church, and, in this case, even against such princes as the counts of Mansfeld, who have introduced the Lutheran Reformation in their countries.

Münzer's justification for this radical procedure against the existing institution of the Church and Christian authority is the Holy Ghost through whom the living God speaks directly to those whom he has chosen. Through Münzer, Joachimitism enters its revolutionary phase in Germany.

During the decisive period of his life, Münzer became acquainted with the writings of Joachim of Fiore, who had proclaimed the coming of the time of the Holy Ghost in which the church establishment would fade away. The relationship between man and God would be raised from the level of the servitude of sons to the level of friends of God. Münzer probably came into contact with the Joachimite doctrine of the Spirit during his stay in Prague. Joachim's ideas had found wide acceptance there, ever since the time of the Hussite movement. Münzer picked up this tradition. The Holy Ghost justifies the new beginning, and Münzer draws the revolutionary consequences.

Paradoxically, the social facet of his revolutionary program is rooted in mysticism as well. The German Church of the early Middle Ages particularly had a largely feudal hierarchy because of the predominant privilege of the aristocracy to appoint the clergy of their churches. The leading positions in the churches were occupied by aristocrats, mostly the second-born of ruling families.[14] The first-born inherited the paternal rights of government, the second son became a cleric and was given a leading spiritual office, that of bishop or abbot. The sovereign disposed of such offices as patron and was quite prone to slip them into the hands of members of his family. Feudalism also prevailed in the monasteries. The great mystics of the fourteenth century were aristocrats. Eckhart was a lord of Hohenheim; Jordan of Saxony was a scion of the family of the counts of Eberstein; Henry Suso the son of a knight, Heinrich von Berg; Mechthild of Magdeburg a descendant of a family of knights; and Mechthild of Hackeborn belonged to the family of the barons of Hackeborn from northern Thuringia.

In mysticism, members of the aristocracy themselves have set aside the aristocratic principle, based on blood relationship, and replaced it by the idea of an aristocracy of the spirit.[15] This was expressed repeatedly by Meister Eckhart: God alone is aristocratic, man only to the extent to which God has conferred aristocracy upon him. Aristocracy conferred by God is the re-establishment of the image of God in man. It comes to pass by the birth of the Son in the soul of faithful man.

We therefore find here a spiritual reinterpretation of the definition of aristocracy. A man is not an aristocrat by virtue of his genealogical descent, but only if God made him an aristocrat. This original aristocracy is the only valid one, but man has lost it by his rebellion against God. Sin and the renunciation of allegiance to God lead to the loss of aristocratic status. Only the birth of the Son in the soul of faithful man reinstates him as an aristocrat.

The spiritual interpretation of the term aristocracy remained a basic theme of German mysticism. Angelus Silesius, in his *Cherubinischer Wandersmann*, deals with the theme of aristocracy in numberous epigrams:

> The ancestors of the wise man are Father, Son, and
>   Spirit.
> If he boasts of his ancestry, he refers to them.[16]

or

> The only man of noble blood
> Is the one whose flesh and soul are brought forth out
>   of God.[17]

It is also possible to give a revolutionary interpretation
to this thought: Before God, all Christians are equal. Before God, external nobility, the rank of aristocracy, does
not count, but only the internal rank reached by having
faith and by being chosen. This spiritual criterion of nobility can also serve as the basis for an attack against the
validity of the legal claims of blood-aristocracy and the
rank of nobility.

Thomas Münzer has drawn the consequences of this
mystical spiritualization: Before God, all men are equal.
Further unchristian insistence upon privileges of rank is
therefore contrary to the will of God. There is another
revolutionary conclusion: The holders of status privileges
are unwilling to surrender them voluntarily as good Christians should. On the contrary, they continue to exploit
burgesses and peasants, they fight against the Gospel,
which is a gospel of equality. Therefore, in God's name,
kill them!

We do not intend to give here a fully detailed description of Münzer's revolution. It ended with the victory of
the allied sovereigns of Hesse, Thuringia, and Brunswick
and with the defeat of the band of rebellious peasants
near Frankenhausen on May 15, 1525. The rebellious
town of Mühlhausen was captured on May 19, 1525. Münzer was executed on May 27.[18]

It is, however, important to note some of the speeches
with which he incited peasants and petty bourgeois to resistance against the Christian authorities. Since he gath-
ered around himself a band of poorly armed and poorly
organized people from the weakest social strata, the decisive thought for him was that the Lord would so

strengthen the weak that they could topple the mighty from their thrones.

As early as in 1523, Münzer wrote to his brethren in Stolberg: "The right reign of Christ must be realized after we are denuded of all ornaments of this world. Then the Lord will come and reign, and he will push all tyrants to the ground. He will give strength to the chosen men who were weak because of their dedication. He will attract them by the strength which emanates from him."

Commenting on the letter in which he scolded the princes, he said:

> I answered them that it would only be fair if the rulers would not act contrary to the faith of Christ. But since they act not only contrary to faith but also contrary to the law of nature, they should be strangled like dogs.[19]

From this angle, the quotation from Jeremiah 20:11, which Münzer mentioned so frequently, assumes a revolutionary meaning:

> But the Lord is with me as a dread warrior;
> Therefore my persecutors will stumble, they will not
>   overcome me.
> They will be greatly shamed, for they will not suc-
>   ceed.
> Their eternal dishonor will never be forgotten.[20]

The older people of our present generation have witnessed a number of bloody revolutions. They know the revolutionary jargon from literature and out of their own experience, but when Münzer used these strong words, they still had the sound of pristine freshness and novelty. Accordingly, they exercised a demagogic fascination. When the struggle reached its climax, revolutionary messianism became wild fanaticism.

In Münzer's Manifesto to the people of Allstedt, sent

at the end of April 1525 from Mühlhausen, he appealed
to them as follows:

> If there are just three of you who, in dedication to
> God, are only looking for his name and honor, then
> even a hundred thousand will not make you fearful.
> Onward then! The time has come! The wicked are
> frightened like dogs. Appeal to the brethren that
> they find peace and keep their testimony. It is of ut-
> most necessity. Onward, onward, onward! Have no
> pity, if Esau gives you kind words, as in Genesis 33.
> Look at the distress of the godless! They will entreat
> so kindly, they will whine and implore like children.
> Have no mercy, as God ordered through Moses in
> Deuteronomy 7 and as he revealed to us too. Make
> your appeals in villages and towns, particularly to the
> miners and other good fellows who could be useful.
> We cannot sleep any longer! . . .
>
> Onward, onward, while the fire is hot! Don't let
> your sword get cold! Don't weaken! Strike the iron,
> cling-clang, on the anvil of Nimrod! Throw their
> tower to the ground! You cannot get rid of your hu-
> man fears while they are still alive. The Word of God
> cannot be preached to you while they are your over-
> lords. Onward, onward, while there is still daylight!
> God walks in front of you, follow him, follow him!
>
> > *Signed:* Thomas Münzer, a servant
> > of God against the godless.[21]

On April 29, 1525, he wrote to the community of
Frankenhausen:

> You must not fear anybody. As the Lord says:
> "Behold, the strength of my poor people shall be in-
> creased." Who will attack them? Therefore be bold
> and put your faith in God alone. Then he will give
> you, as a little group, more strength than you would

believe yourself . . . And don't let kind words per-
suade you to show yellow-bellied compassion. Then
your cause will prevail!

>Signed: The community of Christians
>in the field of Mühlhausen.[22]

In his letter of May 12, 1525, addressed to Count
Ernst von Mansfeld, the sovereign of the district, Münzer
wrote:

>So that you may know we have binding orders, I
>am telling you: The eternal living God has ordered
>us to push you from your throne with the force given
>to us. For you are useless to Christendom. You are a
>pernicious scourge of the friends of God. Of you and
>your ilk, God has spoken in Ezekiel 34 and 39,
>Daniel 7, and Micah 3. Obadiah, the prophet, says:
>"Your nest shall be torn out and crushed." We want
>to have your answer by tonight; otherwise, in the
>name of the Lord of Hosts, we shall punish you.
>Make your decision accordingly. We shall do immedi-
>ately what God has ordered us to do. You do your
>best too. I shall come.

>Signed: Thomas Münzer
>with the sword of Gideon.[23]

In recent years, the connection between revolution and
expectation of the end of time has been the subject of
detailed research, particularly by English and American
sociologists. They investigated the share of chiliastic religious tendencies in the social revolutions of the various
periods of European and American history. Here special
mention should be made of the studies of Norman Cohn
in Cambridge and of those of the Laboratory for Research in Social Relations of the University of Minnesota.

In Germany, Wilhelm Mühlmann of Heidelberg has
dealt most extensively with this question. He has studied

the connection between chiliastic religious expectations and social-revolutionary movements among the African Negroes and the natives of the Pacific islands. The resulting studies of the sociology of revolution were submitted in his work *Chiliasmus und Nativismus, Studien zur Psychologie, Soziologie und historischen Kasuistik der Umsturzbewegungen* (Berlin, 1961).

The conclusions which Mühlmann reaches in his systematic, final chapter are largely applicable to Münzer too: "The tendency for revolt was created by the Jewish-Christian doctrine of apocalypse. The principle of rebellion has existed since then. The revelations of Daniel, Enoch, and John were decisive. Prophets and pseudo-prophets have since then interpreted the first and last named again and again in relation to contemporary events."[24]

Mühlmann points out furthermore that chiliasm, the expectation of the thousand-year Kingdom, has, by its intrinsic structure, a tendency to press for action. There are, of course, certain elements in eschatological expectations which tend to retard action, such as the adventist or escapist attitudes. However, all these types of waiting attitudes are still "virtually for action." From a waiting attitude, they can suddenly switch to revolutionary action. The urge to act or not to act will be largely determined by the factual power situation.

Chiliasm can easily underestimate the real power situation. This occurred in the case of Münzer. He believed that a small minority with God on its side would always be a majority. He led his barely organized and poorly armed bands of peasants and petty bourgeois against an army of knights, far superior in discipline and military effectiveness, promising that he would catch the projectiles of the enemy artillery with the sleeves of his coat. There are other, similar cases in the history of chiliastic revolutions.

Besides, Mühlmann confirms the conclusions to which we were led by Joachim's doctrine of the three ages:

> The idea of progress is a secularized form of chili-astic intuition. The chiliast marches toward the Kingdom of God. His social and psychological moti-vation is fundamental change. While following this road, he wants to create something entirely new. The religious substance of such progress can remain in-tact for a long time. But besides, by a straight ad-vance on the path of history progress falls apart into various secular tendencies. Revolution, as revolt against the existing order, is the strongest among them, because it is sustained by the chiliastic inner structure. In revolution, the urge for progress be-comes itself progressive, that is, it continually by-passes the maximal profit of whatever has been achieved. Everything is only a step toward a "plus" whether it be in power, prestige or property. We are still at this stage today—the substance of religion continues to work. The most important continuation of chiliasm is not the history of the sects but rather the political Utopias which have taken over the her-itage of Christian chiliasm.

V

Darwin's Theory of Evolution and Its Effect upon the Christian Expectation of the End of Time

The decisive turning point for an understanding of man and history came when the idea of evolution, as developed by natural science, penetrated into nineteenth-century anthropology.

The idea of evolution as such was not new. From the beginning, the Christian understanding of man was determined by something akin to an idea of evolution. The idea of deification, the Christian concept of the superman itself, developed out of the idea of growth, evolution, and transformation of man's spiritual powers. But growth was always seen on the spiritual level, as a Christian's progressive formative development toward the "perfect man" (Eph. 4:13), a growth of the supernatural intellectual faculties.

It is generally taken for granted, nowadays, that the term evolution first came to the fore in modern natural science, within biology, botany or zoology. But this is not correct. In the language of philosophy and in the general consciousness of modern times, the term evolution was first introduced as the dialectical antithesis of revolution. The external cause for this was the intellectual reaction in Germany to the French Revolution, the first movement involving a violent overthrow which designated itself with the modern political term "revolution."

Strange as it may appear, the term revolution did not get its modern meaning of violent political overthrow of the existing order of State and society until the French Revolution. As late as the seventeenth century, it had exactly the opposite connotation of overthrow, namely, the orderly circulation of the stars, particularly the revolution—*revolutio*—of the planets around the sun. The term received its modern meaning by a gradual change of its original significance resulting from astrology and a combination of the movements of the stars with Aristotle's doctrine of the State. This doctrine suggested that there was a cyclical sequence of forms of government, from democracy to tyranny, and that the changes were effected by political struggles. These changes in the forms of government, which were mostly brought about by force, were related to certain constellations in their movement, that is, revolution.

The prevailing mood of intellectual Germany, concerning the French Revolution, was formulated at the time by Herder: "My motto is: continuous, natural, and reasonable evolution of matters, not revolution."[1] The French Revolution and its political interpretation of the term revolution also led Kant to a confrontation of evolution and revolution. After 1789, Kant followed "the Revolution of an ingenious people at the border of Germany as a step along the path which he had designed" with "interest . . . bordering on enthusiasm."[2] On the other hand, he expected progress for his own country only "by way of evolution, from above, not by incitement of the people and not by insurrection."[3]

The term evolution was introduced into the terminology of German idealism especially by Franz von Baader. In his case, too, it appears in its dialectical relationship with the term revolution as exemplified in the French Revolution. This is expressed most clearly in Von Baader's work *Über den Evolutionismus und Revolutionismus*, published in 1834. His definition of evolution is developed by a dialectical comparison with the political and philosophical meaning of revolution.

The decisive point is that Herder as well as Kant and particularly, later on, Franz von Baader, used the term evolution as a category of history and not of the natural sciences. Historical evolution, the gradual development of new political conditions out of a given basis, is the antithesis to forcible overthrow and violent implementation of an intellectually conceived new program.

Von Baader even uses the term evolution in a sense which is connected with the history of salvation—it stands for the development from the Old Testament to the New Testament phase of the history of salvation. He calls "the law of Sinai only a preparation for the law of the Spirit which would have developed freely out of it,"[4] and applies it also to the total course of the history of salvation. In his book *Revision der Philosopheme der Hegelschen Schule bezüglich auf das Christentum* (1839), he states that it is "a major crime of past scriptural interpretations that the historical factor is not brought into proper focus. Yet, it is this factor to which Scripture points distinctly for the successive evolution of man and nature, to which man is so closely tied."[5] Later, he even refers to this general evolution of the history of nature and of salvation as "that evolution toward the light, the stages of which cut across the history of the individual, of mankind, and of nature."

Von Baader was already familiar with the "Christ of Evolution" whom we will find again in the works of Teilhard de Chardin. By his appearance in the historical form of Jesus, Christ has created a new element for the future existence of humanity in history. He develops, within history, toward his future perfection. Jesus Christ himself is not "a revolutionary abolition of the Law," but rather "its evolutionary fulfillment."[6] He is only the beginning of a future development of mankind. "Christ was in full possession of those treasures of God. But he displayed them only very gradually before our eyes. He will progress steadily in this evolution, to the end of time, when he will again affirm man's reunion with God."[7]

This definition of evolution which belongs to history, in fact, to the history of salvation, was developed out of the Christology and anthropology of the New Testament itself. It was, therefore, part of the intellectual tradition of European philosophy before its use in natural science by the followers of Darwin and Lamarck in the second half of the nineteenth century. It must not be overlooked that this historical and even eschatological connotation of the term evolution appears among natural scientists whenever they leave the territory of pure scientific research and try to deduce from it a general philosophical or ideological system.[8]

This fact leads to the general conclusion that this term could only have developed against the background of Christian thought. In the thinking of antiquity, a certain pattern of historical evolution was known. It related the historical development of states and empires to the sequences in the age of man: childhood—youth—mature manhood—and old age. But this "evolutionary" process too was imbedded in cyclical thinking and in the basic idea of perpetual return. The idea of working toward a definite goal in evolution emerged only in Christian thinking on time and history. Only the Christian understanding of God knows of a beginning and end of history, of an inner connection between the realization and self-manifestation of God as Creator and Lord of the history of salvation. Only the Christian understanding of God knows of a divine plan, which is being implemented both in the history of nature and of salvation, a plan which is directed toward one distinct goal as its purpose. Only the Christian understanding of God knows of the co-ordination and convergence of all developments toward the one goal of the final condition in which "God will be everything to every one" (I Cor. 15:28).

The application to man of Darwin's natural-science idea of evolution led to a dual and contradictory appraisal of man himself. On the one hand, it actually involved a very dramatic devaluation of man. The traditional anthropology of the Church had tended to neglect, ever increasingly, the purely corporeal aspect of man; it saw in man a unique creature endowed with a soul, whose salvation was the focal point of world history. Now, man was suddenly considered from the biological-corporeal aspect only and appeared as one single species within the category of mammals, as a being who, by his biological descent, belonged to the animal kingdom.

Darwinism has, in fact, belatedly brought to anthropology the great change which Copernicus had brought three hundred years earlier to cosmology. The biblical image of the universe had the earth and man at its center. Copernicus' image of the universe had removed the geocentric point of view of the Bible, but theology had hardly paid any attention to it. It had continued to leave man as the central figure of the universe of creation, both in cosmology and in its history. This is now questioned by Darwin. In the total line of evolution of life, man appears as a late variety of the higher mammals, as a product of a process of selection developing on the basis of certain laws which natural science can formulate.

But this is only one aspect of the doctrine that "man is a descendant of the ape." In the consideration of the ideological effects of Lamarckism and Darwinism upon the intellectual history of the nineteenth century, there was a rather one-sided emphasis on the devaluation of man. At the same time, the application of the doctrine of evolution upon man gave rise to an emphatically optimistic and higher evaluation of man. This can be attributed to the original connotation of the term evolution,

namely, its connection with eschatology and the history
of salvation.

This attitude is foreshadowed during the period of the
Enlightenment. Within German Protestantism, Berthold
Heinrich Brockes (1680–1747) was one of the founders
of popular natural theology in the eighteenth century.
A year after his death, one of his works was published
under the title *Physikalische und moralische Gedanken
über die drey Reiche der Natur*. In this book, we find a
poem on the monkey which is remarkable in many
respects.

The Monkey

If, among all the animals, one appears to have been
created for our amusement and admiration, it is certainly the monkey.

Not only the way his body is built, but also his
facial expressions, his gestures, his adroit actions, his
liveliness and shrewdness, the kind and variety of
strange gestures make it almost appear, as if, to a degree, he could be considered one of us.

Since his actions are so odd, a monkey could even
be a worthy subject for the meditations of a philosopher.

If you give much thought to the instincts which
can be discovered in monkeys, and see how far their
physical and mental faculties go, our reason will almost be startled about these animals.

There we will see the order and ranks of nature by
which these animals seem to come closer to our level
than our pride would permit.

Thus a monkey can also be useful by leading us to
humility. And this makes us think of the following:

What must be the size of the spiritual ladder which
has so many rungs upwards and downwards! We al-

most lose our reason because we cannot see its end.

I cannot talk further about the actions which they can imitate so cleverly, nor about those which they accomplish themselves, because the variety is too great.

This is why I only want to make the observation that they too have been created for our good.

As it is incumbent upon me, I therefore turn to thanks and admiration, and honor the Creator in them, as in all his works.[9]

These thoughts of the pious Hamburg school inspector on the respective rank of man and monkey on the rungs of the "spiritual ladder" found their secular confirmation and scientific underpinning in the theory of descent which was combined with the theory of progress.

The history of evolution was used to prove the idea of progress in anthropology. Now it also became possible to interpret imperfections of the human species in its present shape as being due to the interim character and growth of humanity which is on the road toward a more perfect form.

The outlook into the future was neglected by the official state church. A futuristic image of the "New Man" and of the "New Humanity," although contracted by reinstating an understanding of man, is gaining acceptance in a secularized but highly revolutionary way which holds promise for the future. This development is based on the natural-science idea of evolution and some of its auspices are consciously anti-Christian.

Only now, the idea of evolution is applied to modern man in a thoroughly optimistic way, full of faith in the future. This modern man is not the last and highest form of the human species. He is currently the final product of an infinitely long chain of development and lineage, but is expected to convert himself, in the foreseeable future, into a still better, still higher and more perfect form of man, a "New Man," a "superman." This will be achieved by a controlled direction of evolution itself.

The peculiar dual aspect of judging man is also apparent in the works of Charles Darwin. Darwin refused, on principle, to take a stand on metaphysical or religious questions in his works, or to draw ideological conclusions from his discoveries in the field of natural science. Yet in his private letters, and also in his short *Autobiography*, there are some indications of such conclusions. Darwin's appraisal of the future development of man is very optimistic.

"Believing as I do that man in the distant future will be a far more perfect creature than he now is, it is an intolerable thought that he and all other sentient beings are doomed to complete annihilation after such long-continued slow progress." But then he continues: "To those who fully admit the immortality of the human soul, the destruction of our world will not appear so dreadful." It appears that he does not count himself among those who share this belief.[10]

Equally optimistic are the conclusions of his work on *The Descent of Man and Selection in Relation to Sex:* "Man may be excused for feeling some pride at having risen, though not through his own exertions, to the very summit of the organic scale; and the fact of his having thus risen, instead of having been aboriginally placed there, may give him hope for a still higher destiny in the distant future."[11] This prophecy would give all future prophets of the superman the right to refer to Darwin as their authority, even though he himself never used the term.

On the other hand, the same Darwin makes a few remarks in which the connection of the origin of man with the lower forms of life of the animal kingdom gives rise to a rather resigned outlook on man. He also looks rather skeptically upon all human knowledge purporting to have found a higher meaning in the life of the universe. Thus he once admits to his friend W. Graham his "innermost conviction" that "the universe is not the result of chance. But then with me the horrid doubt always arises whether convictions of man's mind which has developed from the mind of the lower animals, are of any value or at all trustworthy. Would any one trust in the convictions of a monkey's mind, if there are any convictions in such a mind?"[12]

Here we witness how Darwin mobilizes his own knowledge of natural science against his emotional inclination for a religious interpretation of the universe. He mobilizes his reason against his heart. He admits that his "innermost conviction" suggests to him the faith in an inner meaning of creation. But immediately, doubt, born out of scientific knowledge, pulls the flight of his metaphysical dreams down to the level of the factual. He remembers that the human mind which produces such convictions is itself only a product of evolution from the lowest types of animals. Should the moral and religious convictions of the human mammal be credited with a higher degree of objective truth than the "convictions" which a monkey acquired as a result of heredity?

The same doubts are expressed in an even profounder way in Charles Darwin's *Autobiography:*

Another source of conviction in the existence of God, connected with the reason and not with the feelings, impresses me as having much more weight. This follows from the extreme difficulty or rather impossibility of conceiving this immense and wonderful universe, including man with his capacity of looking far backwards and far into futurity, as the result of blind chance or necessity. When thus reflecting, I feel compelled to look to a First Cause . . . ; and I deserve to be called a Theist. . . . But then arises the doubt—can the mind of man, which has, as I fully believe, been developed from a mind as low as that possessed by the lowest animals, be trusted when it draws such grand conclusions? May not these be the result of the connection between cause and effect which strikes us as a necessary one, but probably depends merely on inherited experience? Nor must we overlook the probability of the constant inculcation in a belief in God on the minds of children producing so strong and perhaps an inherited effect on their brains not yet fully developed, that it would be as difficult for them to throw off their belief in God, as for a monkey to throw off its instinctive fear and hatred of a snake.[13]

When applying the doctrine of descent and evolution to man, the question as to which of the two possible interpretations finally prevails is, in the last analysis, a question of the temperament and mood of the particular scholar and writer of the Darwin school.[14] In the end, Darwin seemed to lean in the direction of the pessimistic interpretation. Among his disciples, the optimists who believe in progress are predominant. They are intoxicated by the "New Man" of the future.

Let us listen to some of these voices. David Friedrich Strauss belongs to the most enthusiastic adherents of Darwin in Germany. He has given rather drastic expression to the above-mentioned two interpretations—quite a popularized version thereof, of course—:

> So, here we are, having reached the notorious theory of man's descent from the ape. It is a *sauve qui peut*, not only for the world of true believers and for men with tender feelings, but also for many an individual who is otherwise reasonably free of prejudice. Whoever does not find that this theory is god-

less, or believes at least that it is in poor taste? If it is not considered contrary to the dignity of revelation, it will at least be looked upon as an outrage against human dignity.

We allow everybody to have his own taste. We know that there are many who have more respect for a count or baron gone to waste by his slovenliness than for a commoner who has reached the top by his talent and industry.

Our taste is the reverse. We feel that humanity has much more reason to be proud of having gradually worked itself up by the continuous effort of innumerable generations from miserable, animal beginnings to its present status. We prefer this to being the descendants of a couple, who, after having been created in the image of God, were kicked out of Paradise and to knowing that we are still far from having reached the level from which they fell in the beginning. Nothing dampens courage as much as the certainty that something we have trifled away can never be entirely regained. But nothing raises courage as much as facing a path, of which we do not know how far and how high it will lead us yet.[15]

The self-consciousness of the traditional Christian is determined by the dogma of original sin. Strauss compares it ironically with the self-consciousness of a baron who has gone to waste by slovenliness. He expounds the faith in the constant progress of man toward higher development in the future.

Thus the application of the idea of evolution to the present species of man leads by itself to the expectation of a man of the future who will be nobler, better, greater, and more highly developed. Such a perfect, or super, man can be expected with a fair degree of certainty—as these particular thinkers suppose—if present humanity contin-

ues to develop according to the laws which led it to its
present heights.[16]

Unfortunately, there has been little research so far into
the anthropology of the Darwinists and Lamarckists and
into its influence upon the philosophical anthropology of
the nineteenth century. The question of the nature of
man became too entangled with the current polemics between conservative church circles, on the one hand, and
social democrats and communists, on the other. As a
result, the struggle was mostly fought on the level of political and church propaganda and was reduced to sim-
plified, polemical, and propagandist catch phrases. However, upon looking at this issue more closely, one does
find everywhere in the Darwin-influenced anthropology
the basically optimistic mood of the idea of progress and
the prognosis of the "superman."[17]

As an object lesson, we may mention a philosopher
whose influence upon Nietzsche's thinking on natural science has been proven, namely, Ludwig Büchner (1824–
99). In 1868, Ludwig Büchner published in Leipzig his
Sechs Vorlesungen über die Darwin'sche Theorie. One of
his subject matters was the question of the future perfection of mankind: "I cannot tell you where this progress
will eventually lead. But this much seems to be certain
to me: that nothing will be impossible to man, if he will
use his entire reason and strength. It seems to us that
he is destined to a development of his faculties and to a
sway over nature which will go far beyond the boundaries
drawn by nature at the present time."[18]

In this connection, Büchner refers to the opinions of
the English Darwinist Alfred Russel Wallace (1823–1913)
on the future of mankind, who writes:

> While his external form will probably ever remain
> unchanged, except in the development of that per-
> fect beauty which results from a healthy and well-

organized body, refined, and ennobled by the highest intellectual faculties and sympathetic emotions, his mental constitution may continue to advance and improve till the world is again inhabited by a single homogeneous race, no individual of which will be inferior to the noblest specimen of existing humanity. Each one will then work out his happiness in relation to that of his fellows; perfect freedom of action will be maintained, since the well-balanced moral faculties will never permit any one to transgress on the equal freedom of others; restrictive laws will not be wanted, for each man will be guided by the best of laws; a thorough appreciation of the rights, and a perfect sympathy with the feelings, of all about him; compulsory government will have died away as unnecessary (for every man will know how to govern himself), and will be replaced by voluntary associations for all beneficial public purposes; the passions and animal propensities will be restrained within those limits which are most conducive to happiness; and men will have at length discovered that it was only required of them to develop the capacities of their higher nature in order to convert this earth, which had so long been the theatre of their unbridled passions, and the scene of unimaginable misery, into as bright a paradise as ever haunted the dreams of seer or poet.[19]

Büchner then continues:

If this theory should be correct, gentlemen—personally I do not agree to all its points and I only gave you a very general outline—then it would give many of you ample compensation for the supposed loss of human dignity by our species through the application of the theory of transformation. Even this theory does not really promise us that, in the spirit of eternal progress and Darwinian natural selection, we will develop into some kind of angels with wings at our shoulders. Yet looking into the future of mankind holds more satisfaction for our pride than looking back into its past.[20]

Büchner tries hard to deflect our imagination from the image of a future development of man into a superhuman being "with angels' wings at its shoulders." But that image of his own fancy, showing the final stage which man will reach on the way to higher development, the image of "as beautiful a paradise, as prophets and poets have ever dreamed of," is not far removed from the wishful image of the superman: "The further man is removed from his animalistic origin and relationship, the more he replaces the unlimited sway nature held over him by his own free and reasonable decisions, the more he will become a man in the true sense of the word and the closer he will approach those goals which we consider the future of man and humanity."[21]

Finally, it is very interesting to look at these images of the future, mentioned by Büchner, as they were developed by Alfred Wallace, an English scholar who held no official appointment but had gained great fame by his books *Travels on the Amazon and Rio Negro* and *Palm Trees of the Amazon*.[22] In his *Contributions to the Theory of Natural Selection* he also included a treatise on *The Development of Human Races under the Law of Natural Selection*.

This treatise, in which Wallace draws the conclusions for anthropology from Darwin's theory on the descent of man, has a chapter entitled: "The Bearing of Natural Selection upon the Future Development of Man." In it, Wallace wants to "give an answer to those people who claim that, if Mr. Darwin's theory of the origin of species were correct, the shape of man would have to be subject to changes as well and should assume different forms. This form would be as different from his present being as he is from a gorilla or chimpanzee. They speculate what kind of a form this would likely be."[23]

Possibly the most striking feature of this breakthrough of eschatological elements into the science of anthropology is that, from the beginning, spiritistic and parapsychological elements emerge and determine the concept of the future development of mankind. Wallace, the disciple of Darwin, was an early spiritist. He was convinced that humanity was in a phase of development which would be followed by an evolutionary leap into the realm of spirits. People like Büchner acknowledged this fact with some alarm. But there was a similar development in Germany. Parapsychology took an interest in the theory of evolution and considered it the scientific basis for its assumption that, in the next stage of evolution, man would develop his faculties of extrasensory perception and communication to their highest perfection and for general use. In some extreme and exceptional cases, such faculties are even found now from time to time.

It is significant that the founder of parapsychology and of the Society for Scientific Psychology (1889), Baron Carl Du Prel, expressed himself along these lines. He emphasized the necessity of developing precise methods of control, developed by natural science when carrying on research in the field of parapsychology. He was convinced that the future development of man would lead to an increase and an intensification of his capacity to handle his paraphysical faculties consciously and in a controlled manner. In his biographical introduction to the *Seherin von Prevorst*, he writes:

It is Darwinism which leads us to mysticism. In its theory of perception, exact natural science has proved that we live among many things which we cannot

see. It forgot to add that, in the case of exceptional
individuals, the emotional threshold may be mobile.
This should help us to gather rather remarkable information about the world.

The prophetess of Prevorst was such an individual.
She lived in a world which was closed to us. One
could almost say that she foreshadowed the man of
the future. In her, something manifested itself which
otherwise only a biological intensification could have
achieved, namely, a shift of the emotional threshold.
She lived in closer union with nature than the rest
of us. Metals and plants, animals and men affected
her in a way which we cannot fathom.[24]

A visionary of the type of the prophetess of Prevorst
is thus described here as an anticipation of future man, as
the next stage of human evolution which we can expect.
At that stage, the parapsychic faculties which she had, as
an individual, will be realized by "biological intensification" in a general, consciously controllable way.

Faith in man's capacity for future development also inspired poets and thinkers, particularly of the Anglo-Saxon
world. Almost invariably, the spirited expressions which
are used in applying the idea of evolution to man are
connected with an outlook for a superman of the future.
Quite often, this occurs in a rather surprising context.

Thus we find this faith in a future higher development
of man, for which no support could be found in contemporary Christian anthropology, in the works of a
writer and thinker like Lafcadio Hearn, who was concerned
with Buddhist ideas, particularly the idea of the Bodhi-
sattva and the doctrine of reincarnation.

In *Kokoro* Hearn writes about his contact with Japa-
nese Buddhism:

What we may allow ourselves to believe, with the
full consent of Science, is that marvelous revelations

await us. Within recent times new senses and powers have been developed—the sense of music, the ever-growing faculties of the mathematician. Reasonably it can be expected that still higher unimaginable faculties will be evolved in our descendants. Again it is known that certain mental capacities, undoubtedly inherited, develop in old age only; and the average life of the human race is steadily lengthening. With increased longevity these surely may come into sudden being, through the unfolding of the larger future brain, powers not less wonderful than the ability to remember former births. The dreams of Buddhism can scarcely be surpassed, because they touch the infinite; but who can presume to say they never will be realized?[25]

In natural science, the theory of evolution has retained its optimistic outlook for the future evolution of man. This applies also to its most modern representative, Julian Huxley. Strangely enough, he deliberately turns to Buddhist ideas and forms of meditation and expects an increase of the parapsychic capacities of man.

Huxley declares that fully developed human personalities are the "highest products of evolution."[26] They have reached greater capacities and a higher degree of organization than any other part of matter in this world. The general development of life has thus found fulfillment in man whose own development is not yet concluded. But, in its present stage, it already indicates future possibilities of development. Elements of further development are "the development of inherent capacities by the individual, and of new possibilities through the human race, the satisfaction of spiritual and material needs, the emergence of new capacities of experience, and the building of personalities."[27] Looking at past stages of development shows us the "need to keep human development open for the realization of new possibilities."[28]

In the process of future evolution, the co-operation of mature individuals in teams, their fusion into a kind of collective superbrain, plays an important part. Within this process, Julian Huxley attributes special importance to the methods of religious training of the inner life, as practiced by the mystics of all religions, particularly by those who practice Yoga. The states of mind reached by the mystics show "what transcendent states of inner peace and unity of spirit the human personality is capable of."[29]

Through systematic study of these possibilities of spiritual development Huxley expects to obtain an important contribution to the formation of a method for spiritual training. With the help of such a method, the results of the mystical practices of the past could be made accessible to a larger public.

The basic mood in his book *Evolutionary Humanism* is therefore optimistic. He also hopes that direction can be given to human evolution in the future by the instrumentality of eugenics. Voicing distinct hope for the success of eugenics, practiced on a broad scale, he says: "But already on the basis of our present knowledge, the eugenic idea can become an incentive and a hope."[30]

As he speaks of the future development of mankind, Huxley also expects that the paraphysical faculties of extrasensory perception and communication will be developed further and become practical and manageable methods of perception and communication for future man. This, he hopes, would be the essential contribution of psychological and parapsychological studies.

This optimistic basic trend has remained dominant in Anglo-Saxon anthropology. In the United States, in particular, it was associated with the idea of technological progress. Edgar Saltus, an American utopian living at the turn of the century, to whom H. G. Wells referred frequently in his book *The Future in America*, says, when describing the view from a newly built skyscraper on Broadway in New York City in 1906: "Evolution has not halted. Undiscernibly but indefatigably, always it is progressing. Its final term is not existing buildings, nor in existing man. If humanity sprang from gorillas, from humanity gods shall proceed . . . The story of Olympus is merely a tale of what might have been. That which might have been, may yet come to pass. Even now could the old divinities, hushed forevermore, awake, they would be perplexed enough to see how mortals have exceeded them."[31]

The methods we used up to the present in applying the theory of evolution upon man and his future were all within the area of natural science. But everywhere they show the original theological heritage which had as its sources the Christian expectation of the end of time and, indeed, the history of salvation.

VI

The Marxist and Materialistic Interpretation of the History of Salvation

The meeting of Marxism and Darwinism occurs to the accompaniment of a literary drumbeat. It can be dated precisely since it was Friedrich Engels who first reported to his friend Karl Marx on his reading of Darwin in a letter dated December 12, 1859. It is quite significant that he does not simply write a report on Darwin's book *Origin of Species by Means of Natural Selection* (1859), which he must have read in London soon after the publication of the first English edition. Instead, he begins with an uncommonly aggressive satirical application of the theory of descent upon two German colleagues and collaborators in the socialist camp. They are Beltziech (Beta), editor of the weekly *How Do You Do?*, and Gottfried Kinkel, a friend of Freiligrath's. Apparently, reading Darwin stimulated his journalistic imagination particularly. His method of applying the theory of descent polemically illustrates very well the vulgar style of correspondence of these two protagonists of communism. It operates extensively with fecal invective:

> Dear Blackie . . . Beta (Bettziech) is the greatest scoundrel I ever met. The trashy article really made me mad. Unfortunately, the fellow is such a cripple that you cannot knock him more crooked than he is already. But somebody will have to take personal revenge on that dog, some time. It will always be a source of satisfaction, though, that a beautiful soul like Kinkel has to find its complement in such a dirty

pig. What a sequence of crippled moles, who have chosen shit as their element of life, must be brought to the highest degree of garbage-existence by Darwin's *natural selection* before a single Bettziech can be produced.[1]

After this boorish application of the theory of descent (in reverse) upon his colleagues, he proceeds to characterize the principles of Darwin: "Incidentally, I am just reading Darwin and find him excellent. One side of theology had not been smashed yet. This has happened now. Never before has such a magnificent attempt been made to show the development of history in nature, at least never as felicitously. We must, of course, bear with the crude English method."[2]

In the midst of this boorish polemic, we see here the lion's claw. With one ingenious glance, Engels has summarized the importance of Darwin into a few cogent sentences.

(1) Darwin has "smashed theology." Engels felt intuitively that idealistic anthropology and its thesis that man is the purpose of the divine plan for the world, that the goal of the creation of the universe was the creation and perfection of man, could not be maintained any longer because of Darwin's theory of descent. Darwin appears to confirm his own criticism of Hegel's Christian anthropology.

(2) Equally by intuition, Engels understands the new method of observation which Darwin introduces with his theory of descent: The application of the terms of history to the universe, the extension of the category of history to events of nature, the understanding of the development of nature as history.

This really tells the whole story: Human history is considered a continuation of natural history. The idealistic trimmings, which presented it as the teleological self-realization of the Absolute Spirit, are removed. It becomes a continuation of natural history with all its real, materialistic premises.

It is surprising to see Engels' spontaneously favorable reaction to the historical interpretation of the processes of nature, which is inherent in Darwin's theory of evolution. Evolution as the history of nature—this idea makes it possible to fit human history into the "history" of nature, as Darwin understands it, namely, as an extension of the process of *natural selection*. The decisive point is that Darwin's theory of evolution is considered, a priori, as a refutation of the Christian, teleological interpretation of history which considers soteriology, the history of man's divine redemption, an extension of the history of creation and original sin.

From the beginning, Marxists considered Darwin as an apologist for their own materialistic theory of the development of human society. It could be easily reconciled with the materialistic interpretation given in Darwin's theory of evolution.

It took some time until "Blackie," his friend Karl Marx, reacted to Engels' brief reference to the discovery of Darwin. He was overworked and did not find the time, at first, to follow up his friend's suggestion. The difficulties which piled up for him at the end of 1860 forced him rather reluctantly to take a rest and it was then that he finally found the leisure to read Darwin himself. His comment on the book is summarized in a sentence of equally ingenious brevity contained in a letter to his friend Engels, dated December 19, 1860. Almost a year after receiving the Engels letter with the first information on Darwin, Marx says: "During those last four weeks of my time of trial, I did a lot of reading. Among others, I read Darwin's book on *Natural Selection*. Despite its crude English presentation, this book establishes the basis for our theory in natural history."[3]

With a single, violent sentence Darwin's doctrine of natural selection is annexed as the ideological basis for dialectical materialism. This annexation, which Karl Marx carried out himself, determined the fate of Darwinism in Central Europe. From then on, Darwinism appeared to be an integral part of Marxist-communist-materialistic ideology. It became the foundation of the socialist image of the world. All communists, all adherents of cremation, all "friends of nature," all materialists and supporters of the idea of materialistic science referred to Darwinism. It became part of the socialist-communist credo.

Karl Marx did not think too much of the details of Darwin's theory of descent after he had intuitively appropriated it. In his writings, there are repeated indications which show his crude appropriation of Darwin's doctrine. He has never discussed Darwinism on the basis of any principle, but he always takes a primitive form of Darwinism for granted. In his "Critique of the Gotha Program of the German Social Democrats" (1885), he says, for example: "What is useful work? Obviously, only work which produces the intended useful effect. A savage—and man is a savage after he has ceased to be a monkey—who kills an animal with a stone or who collects fruit, etc., does 'useful work.' "[4]

Here we see that the point which links Darwinism and Marxism is Darwin's theory of the struggle for existence. The idea of evolution per se is the logical antithesis to the idea of revolution. For a century, the protagonists of German idealism have successfully opposed evolution to revolution (see above, pages 64 ff.). But the idea of the struggle for existence connects Marx's dialectical materialism with Darwin's continuation of the struggle for existence within human history and within the evolution of the human species.

The adoption of a materialistically interpreted Darwin by Karl Marx and his followers had the effect that the entire communist anthropology became dominated by a materialistically interpreted Darwinist theory of evolution. In the Bolshevik museums of the godless, in the introductory chapters of the atheistic schoolbooks of the countries of the Eastern bloc, on the blackboards of Soviet-Russian schools, wherever the development of man is shown in pictures, Darwinism presents itself in the unendingly repeated cliché of the tables showing the descent of man.

In a row of pictures presented either by impressive drawings or, in the larger museums, by dummies made of papier mâché you see first a gorilla, with an evil look in his eye, arms with clenched fists pressed against a hairy chest. Next comes the Neanderthal man, with a protruding lower jaw and receding forehead, a wedge or cudgel in his right hand. He is followed by *homo sapiens*, a hunter and tiller of the soil. Finally, we see the blond *homo socialis* as the last in the row of witnesses of evolution. His forehead is high and he looks confidently into the socialist future, which will be a better future, no doubt.

Engels' first impulse was a negative application of evolution, upon "crippled moles who have chosen shit as their element of life." But in Marxism, the optimistic prognosis for evolution toward socialist progress prevailed. We notice here that evolution has its own logic. Despite the possibility of a pessimistic and negative interpretation, it turns automatically to a positive one, anticipating that evolution will lead to progress, higher development and an upward movement.

The followers of "socialist Humanism" often fought quite strongly against the attempt to attach the superman to *homo humanus* as the next stage of evolution. In an informative treatise entitled "Übermensch, übermenschlich," D. Tschizewskij has pointed out that both terms are found in the works of the leftist Hegelians.[5]

Moses Hess attacked the contemporary leftist Hegelian philosophers because they destroyed the term "man." Particularly in his essay "Die letzten Philosophen,"[6] he criticizes the "leftists" for saying that they all have an ideal which is either higher or lower than man. On the other hand, he points out that in the order of values man assumes a position of his own, a specifically "human" position. Therefore, all attempts to build an ideal social system on a basis which is superhuman, lower than human, or generally inhuman are doomed to failure from the beginning since they ignore human nature and all that is specifically human.

In 1845 Hess blames the social reformers of the left for not finding the road to the human "masses." "As long as you do not try to develop your own nature, as long as you do not try to be human instead of superhuman or inhuman, it is only natural that you will become supermen or inhuman (*Unmenschen*). You will look down with contempt upon human nature, which you have not recognized, and you will treat the masses like wild beasts."[7]

Moses Hess thus criticizes the social revolutionaries of his time for being overconcerned with their reform programs and forgetting man himself, for whom these programs were really meant. As a result, they become supermen or inhuman and despise the common man, the "masses." He thus aims at the opinion which considers the revolutionary an individualistic genius and superman, as defined by the *Sturm und Drang* movement.

As we can see from the context, Hess' criticism of the term "superman" is aimed particularly at the ideals of Bruno Bauer, an enemy of the masses and representative of those who are "above the masses." The reference to *Unmensch* is aimed at Max Stirner, the "Unique." The allusion that Bruno Bauer considers himself a superman is favorably received by the leftist Hegelians. In the following year, 1846, the leftist Hegelian journalist Ernst

Dronke published a witty book, *Berlin*, in which he satirized Max Stirner and Bruno Bauer. "'The Unique' and 'The Lonely One.' Only the ridicule and arrogance of philosophy could have the audacity to say that they stand above life . . . Since they stand above life, life itself will reach its goals best by ignoring the purring of the philosophical supermen."[8] Moses Hess also calls Bruno Bauer a "superman."[9]

Strangely enough, early socialists like Hess appear to have Herder as their ally. Herder defended man against the superman and the inhuman. For him, these two terms were identical. Socialist Humanism has its roots in good old Christian idealism of the German classical age. The distinction between Hess and Herder is their fundamentally different attitude toward religion. All early socialists, Moses Hess included, were deeply influenced by the religious philosophy of Feuerbach who saw in religion an ideological self-interpretation of man, which he recognized only because of its human content. For leftist Hegelians, Feuerbach's religious philosophy proved that a superhuman, transcendental world did not exist. All that is superhuman is merely a product of human imagination which has created a fantastic self-interpretation in religion.

Friedrich Engels also uses the terms "superman" and "superhuman" in this negative sense. For him, "superhuman" is synonymous with "of the hereafter." But following Feuerbach, he understands the "hereafter" to be the unreal, the untrue, the mendacious. Therefore, Engels identifies the struggle for man with a struggle against religion and its untruthful and mendacious pretenses to establish, above humanity, an allegedly higher sphere of the superhuman.

> We want to restore to man the stature which he has lost through religion, not in a divine but in a

human sense. Restoring it means simply to awaken
his self-consciousness. We want to remove everything
that calls itself supernatural and superhuman and
thus remove untruthfulness. For the pretenses of the
human and natural to become supernatural are the
root of all lies . . . To see the glory of human nature,
to understand the development of the human species
in history and its irresistible evolution, to realize its
always certain victory over the unreasonableness of
the individual, to secure its triumph over what seems
to be superhuman to support its hard but successful
struggle with nature, to witness the free and independent creation of a new world based on ethical
conditions of life and to recognize the grandeur of
all this, we do not have to call in the abstraction of a
God to whom we attribute all that is beautiful, great,
sublime, and truly human.[10]

David Friedrich Strauss' epoch-making work, *Der alte
und der neue Glaube,* ends on a similar note. He exhorts
his readers at last to turn away from the fictitious world
of an allegedly superhuman revelation and to make the
recognizable nature of the human beings of this world
the point of departure for the ethics of the future: "We
must become and remain aware of the fact that this no-
tion is untenable. This will compel us to seek and find a
firm foothold for our ethical behavior in our new ideology, that is, in the recognized nature of man instead of in
a fictitious superhuman revelation."[11]

Despite these occasional doubts, the prevailing mood
in the camp of the early socialists is optimistic. It con-
centrates its interpretation entirely on the progress,
development, and evolution of man and human society
in this world.

We want to let Eugen Dühring speak for many others.
Dühring had the strongest influence upon the ideological

discussions of his time through his book *Der Werth des Lebens* (1865). In this book, he asks what is going to happen if a certain form of life reaches its highest form of development and thus its own fulfillment. In other words, he asks the question of the decline and extinction of certain species.

He describes the process of development as a creative phenomenon which is necessarily connected with a corresponding process of the destruction of obsolete, old species which have become extinct. Looking at the total process, he arrives at a positive evaluation. To speak of the decline of one species and its removal by another is actually a fallacy. It is arrived at by the comparison of different species which are separated by wide chronological gaps and show a great number of variations. Dühring applies the same idea to the future development of mankind.

A form of life is only fulfilled in the aforementioned way if it is considered as a certain, limited succession of functions which have to reach an end at some time. It is, of course, possible to regard the changes which lead from one type to another as partial destructions and creations, and not as death in the proper sense. But the ordinary death of individuals will play a decisive role in the transformation of group types. A great number of eliminations will occur as a result of the particular death. New combinations of elements can carry out their creative work only under the condition that the necessary destructions take place.

As the new combinations develop, as a result of extinctions and changed blood mixtures or by direct development, the principal point of the entire process will always be the emergence of changed forms. If there is considerable accumulation of changes, if the chronological interval from previous forms is very wide and if therefore a gap of knowledge divides the two compared conditions, then a change can appear to be a completely new creation. The conclusion will then be that a species has become extinct to make room for another one.

In this manner, humanity could eventually be transformed into a more perfect type of living being and would then look back upon the type of man whom we consider most highly developed as upon some extinct species of animal. Whether this will happen in an uninterrupted sequence, leaving behind historical recollections, or whether there will be sequences interrupted by periods of wild growth without culture, we could always speak of a death of the previous type and of a newly created life of the later type. The mortality of the form of humanity known to us has thus been convincingly shown by these changes in real life. The mere thought that there is such a possibility shows that we have no sufficient reason to believe that the type of man we know will prevail forever.[12]

Dühring therefore expects the emergence of an entirely new and more perfect type of humanity which will develop out of the "type of humanity known to us." But he emphasizes that the appearance of such a higher type of man could at best have "the appearance of an entirely new creation." In the final analysis, he refuses to accept the idea of a death of humanity. Quite surprisingly, he agrees here with Teilhard de Chardin and his Christian interpretation of the theory of evolution. His thinking is dominated by the positive aspect of the theory of evolution which, "for the time being," does not point toward the death of humanity, but rather toward the formation of a higher and nobler type of man. In fact, it postulates such a development.

"The death of humanity would come to pass if the development of the laws of nature were to reach a point at which sensitive life would become completely extinct. Since no other sequence of sensitive beings could follow, this would be the real end of all animal life. We have no reasons to predict this particular development for the future with any certainty. On the contrary, the entire course of development points rather to a steady evolution which will not convert humanity into a corpse but rather into a nobler, quite differently equipped species."[13]

To him the struggle for existence is an important means to further the aim of development. For the present type of humanity, the struggle for social existence serves this function. In this regard, Dühring also warns that we should not look exclusively at the negative side. The social struggle for existence has to be evaluated as something positive, as an increase of strength and a boon to higher development.

Although material difficulties of existence sometimes assume frightening proportions, they are, by and large, a creative force. They not only teach larger groups to be industrious; in many respects, they also train the individual's strength which would, otherwise, not have developed to that extent. They harden the courage to live to a point where there is enough strength to face them. They destroy a lot, but there is also a great deal which they create. Like all other chances of death, they must be entered into the calculation as an element of life itself. Thus they are not only an immediate evil, but also an antagonistic method of enhancing the life which succeeds in overcoming them.[14]

Here, too, the message of the superman is actually considered a postulate of "steady development."

In the case of Dühring the idea of evolving present humanity to a more perfect species has a striking connection with his religious philosophy that, in many respects, reminds us of Nietzsche. Nietzsche connects the appearance of the superman with the "death of God," that is, the end of faith in God (see page 118); Dühring associates the emergence of the New Man with the abolition of religion and the end of faith. Both of them were inspired by Feuerbach, as far as their concept of religion was concerned. Both of them have a similar animosity against Christianity. The emergence of new, more perfect, and greater men has a common prerequisite for both of them: the overcoming of religion and the abolition of faith. They consider faith as the root of intellectual servitude, as the slavery of contemporary men.

According to Dühring, great individuals with their superior and self-propagating purpose will be the trailblazers of this development.

However, man has one consolation for the future. The region of unclarified religious establishments has a low level on which matters will not remain forever as far as the people are concerned . . . A knowledge which is built on conscience, a knowledge and purpose which are carried straight to the masses, will take over the entire field, including that part held previously by religion. The field will be taken over, cleared of weeds, tilled, and defended. Such knowledge is not of the prostituted variety by which nations and people are betrayed all over the world. It must be truly popular and stand up for popularization against the monopoly interest of a decadent cast of scholars and pseudo-intellectuals. What nations as a whole cannot do, individuals can do by their superior, self-propagating purpose. Their particular special knowledge, extensive and reliable, as it may be, only remains a tool for a higher and nobler task. In the spirit of that task, an enhanced general understanding will combine with man's best possible impulses to create unity between thought and deed.[15]

Man is "perfect" only if he has overcome religion and the state of servitude it represents.[16] Dühring therefore wants to replace present practices of historical religions, which worship a God or gods, by "the cultivation of a nobler form of humanity, of national character, and of individuality. At the same time man should seek a deeper understanding of that ideology which has been created to bring out his qualities." For this synthetic culture he also establishes a new ideal of martyrdom:

> The most outstanding case in which a better man commits himself in favor of what is most dignified in humanity, is the case in which less important interests and, if necessary, life itself, are sacrificed for a matter of great intellectual importance, such as the support of highly important truths or their realization in the institutions of life. In both cases, a truly admirable martyrdom will result. If we look more closely, we will find that in the modern world of new nations there are better, truer, and more numerous examples of such martyrdom than in the Judeo-Christian past.[17]

According to his opinion, the veneration of "better men," the heroes of a new, ethical martyrdom, will replace the cult of old religions; the more perfect human species of the future will rise out of the "depths" of the old religions and will accelerate the emergence of an ennobled humanity. This expectation of a "new religion" is a secular negative of the Christian expectation of the end of time. The impulses of the latter are still discernible in its antithesis.

The affinity between socialism and Darwinism was not only noticed by the followers of socialism but also by its opponents. The question of the inner relations between socialism and Darwinism played an important role in the famous dispute between Rudolf Virchow and Ernst Haeckel.

When Rudolf Virchow was at the height of his fame, he was the keynote speaker at the Fiftieth Assembly of the Society of German Natural Scientists and Physicians, held in Munich on September 22, 1878. He took advantage of this opportunity to attack Darwin's theory of descent rather violently. He shocked his audience with the prognosis that the combination of Darwinist ideology with socialism would lead to political repercussions in Germany which could be compared to those in France at the time of the Revolution.

"Just imagine," he told the assembly, "what ideas a socialist has nowadays about the theory of descent! Well, gentlemen, this may sound funny to some of you, but it is very serious. I hope that the theory of descent will not bring us all those terrors which similar theories actually brought to our neighbors' country. At any rate, this theory has a rather doubtful side, if it is applied consistently. I hope it has not escaped your attention that socialism has established contact with it. We must make this absolutely clear!"[18]

This attack, carried out before the most prominent representatives of German natural science, aroused the violent opposition of Ernst Haeckel. In a voluminous pamphlet, published in 1878 and called *Freie Wissenschaft und freie Lehre*, he expressed his opposition to Virchow, particularly in the sixth chapter entitled "Deszendenztheorie und Sozialdemokratie."

Haeckel calls Virchow's thesis a malicious defamation

and denunciation: "Just like Darwin and many others, I consider 'social instincts' the original source of ethical development. Apparently this was Virchow's motive in declaring in his opposing address that the theory of descent was a 'socialist theory.' He thus attributes to it the most dangerous and most reprehensible character which a political theory can have nowadays."[19]

Haeckel then proceeds to establish a counterthesis: "Darwinism is anything but socialistic." His reasoning in support of this thesis is somewhat weak, however. He points out that because of the principle of selection, which is at the basis of the theory of descent, only a particularly qualified elite will survive. "This principle of selection is nothing less than democratic. On the contrary, it is aristocratic in the true sense of the term. If therefore, according to Virchow, consistently applied Darwinism has a 'very reprehensible' side for the politician, this could only mean that it discriminates in favor of aristocratic endeavor." In actual fact, though, those in Germany who adopted the shirt-sleeved philosophy of the struggle for existence were not the aristocratic circles but rather those circles of labor and the fourth estate who were committed to Marxism.

This elective affinity soon found an apology from the standpoint of moral philosophy. In 1898 Ludwig Woltmann published a book entitled: *System des moralischen Bewusstseins mit besonderer Darlegung des Verhältnisses der kritischen Philosophie zu Darwinismus und Socialismus*. The ideas he had developed in the fifth chapter, "Die Darwin'sche Theorie und der Socialismus," were again summarized the following year in a publication under the same title.

His basic idea is already formulated in his first book: "The principle of the struggle for existence and of natural selection calls for a comparison with the basic economic postulates of socialism by its inner relationship with them."[20] This was indeed the point of departure for Marx himself, who recognized Darwinism as a welcome ally for his socialist ideology.

Woltmann then continued by criticizing particularly those followers of Darwin who have a bourgeois background:

It is a mistake of almost all bourgeois Darwinists to apply zoological theories mechanically and without any criticism upon human conditions . . . In a liberal economy there is rarely a truly Darwinist struggle for existence which serves the purpose of perfection. On the contrary, it is usually a principle of degeneration . . . For an unprejudiced and informed scholar, the basic idea of socialism is justified by the highest demands of the moral law and natural development . . . Comparatively speaking, socialism is a form of Darwinism on a higher level of the development of life. Biologically, it is a useful and enhanced adaptation of cultural humanity to its conditions of existence and development, inasmuch as it is no longer possible to make a profit without producing.[21]

The marriage between socialism and Darwinism confirmed German churches in their determined rejection of the socialist movement. The Protestant regional churches, which thought in terms of a state church and were politically conservative, were certain from the beginning that Darwinism, socialism, communism, materialism, and atheism were all identical.

Significantly enough, the discussion between Darwinism and Christian ideology was not primarily conducted on the lofty level of theology, but rather on the level of church apologetics. Its documentations were not theological treatises but articles in church publications, highly emotional in tone, and addressed to conventions of pastors. Only very slowly did the debate ascend to the level of an academico-theological discussion.

A case in point is, for example, the Twentieth Convention of German Protestants in Hamburg. The addresses delivered on this occasion were published in Berlin in 1899 under the title: *Die religionsfeindlichen Strömungen der Gegenwart.* The first one, delivered by Professor J. Reinke of Kiel, dealt with "The Attitude of Natural Science toward Religion," while a second address, delivered by Justice W. Kulemann of Brunswick, was entitled: "The Attitude of Socialism toward Religion."

Reinke discusses Darwinism first. Quite obviously alluding to Haeckel's "Riddles of the universe," he says: "It is understandable that Darwin's doctrine was grist for the mill of materialism. Many people became truly intoxicated. They thought they had found the philosopher's stone which could solve even the last riddles of life in a materialistic sense. But, as any intoxication, the Darwinist one was also followed by disenchantment."

The style of ecclesiastico-theological apologetics is represented most impressively by Richard H. Grützmacher. In his collection *Modern-positive Vorträge,* there is a lecture entitled "Evolution oder Offenbarung?" We quote: "We do not intend to arrange a marriage between evolution and revelation into which both parties bring some property. They should rather be considered as irreconcilable opposites. The life of one means the death of the other. Accordingly, it is our task, at this hour, to investigate the significant characteristics of evolution and revelation in various areas and to deduce from them why they cannot be reconciled."[22]

Grützmacher then describes the doctrine of evolution as a sort of counterreligion which aims to negate the specific foundation of revelation in the Christian religion:

Revelation has common characteristics in the three areas of creation, historical, and personal salvation. The same applies to evolution. If you go to its very roots, you will find that it attempts to explain the facts of creation, of historical and personal redemption without God or, in a weaker form, without God's direct or supernatural intervention. Instead, it explains them as coming from natural forces which are immanent in history. The difference between the modern concept of evolution and previously applied natural or godless criteria for the interpretation of things is that the former has absorbed the idea of development. This means that it does not assume a sudden genesis, but a slow and progressive natural development which it carries through in detail. The world has not been changed by including the idea of development in its evolutionary interpretation. Nor has, as many believe, everything that is dangerous and reprehensible entered the world by the concept of development.[23]

What is characteristic and should be fought in the modern doctrine of evolution is its claim of a development that came out of the depths, and the natural explanation of the causes of development without God . . . From nature, this viewpoint is transferred to history. By and large, history is the same as individual life, an intertwinement of secular forces. In principle, it does not make a great deal of difference how this concept is implemented in detail. It could be done by the theories of Kant and Laplace or by the phantasies of Haeckel. The importance of the masses in history could be emphasized or the effects which heroes can have on it. Natural and worldly forces will always remain the driving belt of all events.[24]

The iron fetters which evolutionary unbelief wants to put on Christian faith can only be broken by a return to the foundations of Christian faith in revelation. Creation is the highest revelation of God in nature. This is where any natural explanation fails. From a scientific viewpoint, too, any evolutionary theory is frustrated by creation right in the beginning. Therefore, many a follower of evolution makes a quarter or half-turn in the direction of revelation. But for the further development, he sends the good Lord into retirement rather prematurely . . . Wherever man has learned to recognize all the summits and depths of his life as revelations of Almighty God, there the chains of evolutionism will be broken at the decisive point. What remains to be done for theory is the much more modest task of using its file to cut some smaller rings.[25]

The treatise of Max Reischle follows a similar trend of thought, albeit less emotionally. It is entitled *Wissenschaftliche Entwicklungsforschung und evolutionistische Weltanschauung in ihrem Verhältnis zum Christentum* and was published in Tübingen and Leipzig in 1902.

Reischle also presents Christianity and evolutionistic ideology as completely opposite and mutually exclusive attitudes of mind: "This is it, indeed: either evolutionistic or Christian ideology! The latter is so clearly defined that it is in sharp contrast to all other ideologies. The center of the Christian concept of God and the world is the faith in God who raises and redeems us for his eternal Kingdom."

After enumerating the various doctrines of faith, Reischle continues: "In all these thoughts, there is a sharp contrast to evolutionism, above all to naturalistic evolutionism, even if it takes a certain halo of idealistic thought in the form of monism . . . In this struggle, there can be no peace. It is a struggle for life or death between the faith in God's saving, sacred love and the faith in developing nature."

But Christianity cannot give up opposition to idealistic evolutionism either. "By its concept of God and the world, Christianity opposes evolutionism on principle. This not only applies to the naturalistic and monistic form of evolutionism, but also to the idealistic kind. The question, which of the two sides we should choose, is not just a question of thinking but of faith and thus of conscience and will."[26]

The ardor of the church apologists in rejecting Darwinism and the theory of evolution can be fully understood. We must remember that the principal interpreter of Darwinism in Germany was Ernst Haeckel. He had indeed developed a new anti-Christian religion, called "Monism," which he defended as emphatically as if he were a Galileo threatened to be burned at the stake. His ardor was expressed by an exaggerated anti-Church and anti-Christian argumentation. All we have to do is thumb through his *Gemeinverständliche Werken* to find such passages everywhere. One passage may suffice to indicate the spirit.

In his treatise *Über unsere gegenwärtige Kenntnis vom Ursprung des Menschen*, published in 1898, he says: "The dogma of the personal immortality of the human soul cannot be reconciled with the law of substance—the great 'Law of the Conservation of Matter and Energy.' But the same also applies to the two other great articles of faith, the dogma of the freedom of the human will and the dogma of the existence of a personal God, who resembles man, and is the Creator, Preserver, and Ruler of the world . . . The mystical secondary characters of those principal ghosts dissolve in the clear sunlight of truth which is spread over the 'riddles of the universe' by the law of substance, the theory of descent, and the doctrine of the Pithecanthropus."[27]

Roman Catholic theology has kept aloof from dealing with this task, which has imposed itself upon theology since the middle of the last century. The reason for this attitude was that the doctrine of evolution and the theory of descent were included in the fight against modernism which was opened by Pius IX with his *Syllabus* of 1864. The idea of evolution was thus thrown into a kind of group responsibility together with socialism, materialism, monism, liberalism, free thinking, and support of cremation. Its fate was sealed by the *Syllabus* of Pius X of 1907 and remains unchanged up to the present time. Even the encyclical *Humani Generis* issued by Pope Pius XII on August 12, 1950, contains a new and detailed expression of opposition against the theory of evolution. We quote:[28]

> If we survey those who are outside the fold of Christ, we have no difficulty in discerning the principal trends which a number of learned men have taken. There are those who accept the so-called *system of evolution* without wisdom or restraint, although it has not even been proved irrefutably by the natural sciences. They want to extend it to the origin of all things. Boldly they pay homage to the monistic and pantheistic interpretation that the whole world is subject to continual evolution. The *supporters of communism* eagerly seize upon this opinion, in the hope of defending and preaching their dialectical materialism more effectively while depriving the souls of every theistic idea. . . .
>
> The Magisterium of the Church does not forbid that the theory of evolution concerning the origin of the human body as coming from pre-existent and living matter—but Catholic faith obliges us to hold

that the human soul is immediately created by God
—be investigated and discussed by experts as far as
the present state of sciences and sacred theology allows. But, this must be done so that reasons for both
sides, the positive and the negative, be weighed and
judged with the necessary gravity, moderation, and
discretion; and let all be prepared to submit to the
judgment of the Church to whom Christ has given
the mission of interpreting authentically the Holy
Scriptures and of safeguarding the dogmas of faith
(*Acta Apostolicae Sedis*, vol. XXXIII, p. 506 [No-
vember 30, 1941]). But there are some who go too
far and transgress this freedom of discussion, who
act as if the origin of the human body from pre-
existing and living matter were already fully proved
by the facts discovered up to now and by reasoning
on them, and as if there were nothing in the sources
of divine revelation which demanded the greatest reserve and caution in this controversy.

But as regards another conjecture, namely, the so-
called *polygenism*, the children of the Church by
no means enjoy the same freedom. For those who
believe in Christ cannot agree with supporters of
that opinion who either claim that after Adam there
existed on this earth true men who did not take
their origin through natural generation from him as
from the first parent of all, or who claim that Adam is
merely a symbol for a number of first parents. For it
cannot be shown how such an opinion can be reconciled with what the sources of revealed truth and the
acts of the Magisterium of the Church teach on
original sin, which proceeds from a sin actually committed by an individual Adam, and which, passed on
to all by way of generation, is in everyone as his own
(cf. Rom. 5:12–19; Conc. Trid., sess. 5, can. 1–4).

This encyclical not only declares that the doctrine of evolution cannot be reconciled with the Catholic doctrine of creation; it also maintains the traditional group-responsibility of the doctrine of evolution, dialectical materialism, and communism. The Anti-Modernist Oath, which made it obligatory for every Catholic priest to observe the contents of the *Syllabus* in the exercise of his spiritual ministry, has also contributed to the fact that Roman Catholic theology has not dealt seriously with the doctrine of evolution and its possible theological consequences.[29]

VII

*Darwin's Theory of Evolution and
Nietzsche's Doctrine of the Superman*

When we referred to Darwin and the transformation, by
Darwin's theory of evolution, of the image of the future
of man and of human society, we indicated repeatedly
that Nietzsche's reinterpretation of Christian eschatology
into the anti-Christian vision of the superman is dominated by the Darwinist system. Nietzsche's image of the
superman and its connection with the transformation of
the expectation of the end of time, brought about by
Darwin, play an important role, indeed, in the modern
secularization of Christian eschatology.

The image of the superman which Nietzsche established in his works as a model for the future of man and
humanity has encouraged many pathological characters
to consider themselves supermen. Under this name, they
indulged in their inhuman urges, so that we approach
this subject with some hesitation. The abuse of the term
"superman" by all those who tried to play superman
themselves, in the name of Nietzsche, seems to have com-
promised the name and the cause itself forever.

Yet, more than ever, it is necessary today to clarify
Nietzsche's image of the superman carefully. The possibility of the development of man and humanity is again
discussed, in spite of Nietzsche, in various sectors of the
natural sciences, particularly in anthropology, biology, and
brain research. Because of this, it is necessary to look more
closely at the ideas which that philosopher associated
with the term "superman." Gifted with a mind which

was capable both of cultural criticism and prophecy, Nietzsche put this term into the center of his observations on the future of man and human history.

In a critical discussion with his followers and opponents, he complained quite vigorously that his message of superman was misunderstood.

We find this discussion in *Ecce Homo* of 1888, in the notoriously famous chapter "Why I Write Such Good Books."

> The word "superman" was understood to mean a particularly well-made type, as opposed to "modern" men, to good men, to Christians and other nihilists—this word, if spoken by Zarathustra, the destroyer of morals, becomes a rather thoughtful one. Almost everywhere, it was understood in all innocence as the incarnation of those values of which the figure of Zarathustra represents the very opposite. In other words, it was considered as an "idealistic" type of a higher kind of man, half "saint" and half "genius" . . . As a result, other erudite horned animals have suspected me of Darwinism. Some even recognized the hero cult of Carlyle, that great involuntary and unwitting forger. If I whispered into somebody's ear he should look for Cesare Borgia rather than for Parsifal, he would not trust his own ears.[1]

Nietzsche blames his readers for nothing less than complete misunderstanding of his message of the superman. He names three kinds of such misunderstandings:

1. The interpretation of the superman as "an idealistic type of a higher kind of man, half saint and half genius."

2. An interpretation of the superman in the spirit of Darwin's theory of descent and evolution.

3. In the spirit of Carlyle's hero concept.

Philosophically, the third interpretation is closely linked

with the first one, since Carlyle's hero concept is closely related to the idealistic concept of genius. Thus Nietzsche's complaint boils down to an idealistic and a Darwinist misunderstanding.

The idealistic "misunderstanding" is of lesser importance to us in this connection. There are indeed direct links between the concept of Nietzsche's superman and the idealistic genius.[2] Years before when Nietzsche used the character of Zarathustra to deliver the sermon of the superman, he had made use of the term "superman" in a way which showed the connection with the genius concept of German idealism and the *Sturm und Drang* movement.

As in the case of Jean Paul and Emerson, Napoleon was Nietzsche's model of a historical genius, which he used for his image of the superman in the *Genealogy of Morals:* "Like a last signpost to an alternative route Napoleon appeared, most isolated and anachronistic of men, the embodiment of the noble ideal. It might be well to ponder what exactly Napoleon, that synthesis of the brutish with the superhuman, did represent."[3] Here, Napoleon appears as the political figure who took the decisive step to true superman status.

"Napoleon—an incomparably pleasant feeling pervaded Europe—a genius shall be master."[4] In this connection, as in the case of Jean Paul, Napoleon's status as superman is still interpreted entirely on the basis of the idealistic concept of genius. Both terms—superman and genius—are used interchangeably.

In the criticism of his critics in 1888, Nietzsche complained that his superman had been misunderstood as "an idealistic type of a higher kind of man, half saint and half genius." But when he wrote *Ecce Homo,* he had long forgotten that he himself had described the superman as such an idealistic type, half saint and half genius, when he first conceived it in the *Birth of Tragedy.*

"Neither the state nor the people nor humanity exist for their own sake. The goal lies in their summits, in the great "solitary" ones, the saints and artists, neither before nor behind us, but outside of our time. But this goal definitely points beyond humanity. All this makes it clear that genius does not exist for the sake of humanity, even though it is humanity's summit and final goal."[5]

"Beyond humanity" is still understood entirely in the spirit of idealism and *Sturm und Drang* as a thrust into the dimension of the titanic. The peculiar concept of the final purpose is still missing. It became part of Nietzsche's superman concept by his contact with, and analysis of, the idea of development in contemporary natural science and particularly of Darwin's theory of descent.

It is necessary, in this connection, to quote the first programmatic proclamation of the superman by Zarathustra in the unabridged text:

> I teach you the superman. Man is something that shall be surpassed. What have you done to surpass him? All beings so far have created something beyond themselves. And you want to be the ebb of this great flood and even go back to the beasts rather than to surpass man? What is the ape to man? A laughingstock or a painful embarrassment . . . You have made your way from worm to man, and much in you is still worm. Once you were apes, and even now, too, man is more ape than any ape. Whoever is the wisest among you is also a mere conflict and cross between plant and specter. But do I bid you become specters or plants?
>
> Behold! I teach you the superman!
>
> The superman is the meaning of the earth. Let your will say: the superman shall be the meaning of the earth![6]

This statement would be unthinkable without Darwin. It simply takes Darwin's (misunderstood) theory of descent for granted and builds it into a prophetic criticism of contemporary man. If Nietzsche says, with a glance in the direction of Darwin, "You have progressed along the road from worm to man," he adds emphatically: "and much in you is still worm." If, as a superficial pupil of Darwin, he says: "Once you were apes," he adds no less emphatically: "and man is still more ape than any ape."

But his concept of the superman is also based on Darwin's doctrine of evolution which Nietzsche summarizes in these words: "All beings, until now, created something which went beyond them." This phrase is applied to human beings. But it is immediately transformed into the criticism that contemporary humanity failed in the task imposed upon it—to create something which went beyond them.

Two of Darwin's basic thoughts are still maintained in Nietzsche's concept of the superman: (1) the doctrine of development in its general form and in the specific version of the theory of descent, and (2) the idea of the struggle for existence. Nietzsche refers again and again to the "law of development which is the hope of selection."[7] He also recognizes with equal clarity that the struggle for existence is an essential element within this process of selection.

But we must not overlook two basic differences between Nietzsche and Darwinism. The first one is that Nietzsche's superman is not considered the product of a development in which nature, whose life is governed by the law of evolution, "automatically" produces the new species of superman, which goes beyond the present human species. The superman is rather a product of man's own free creation, in fact, of deliberate breeding. His appearance, therefore, comes into the sphere of freedom and not into the sphere of the laws of nature.

The second point concerns a distinction along the same

lines. The superman is also a product of a struggle. But it is not a struggle for existence in the sense that the weak succumb when fighting for biological self-preservation, but rather in the sense of a free contest.

In the *Birth of Tragedy* Nietzsche says: "The poet overcomes the struggle for existence by idealizing it into a free contest."[8] The struggle for existence is thus lifted out of the sphere of the law of nature into the sphere of freedom. Raising the superman becomes a competitive principle.

All of Nietzsche's criticism of Darwin originates in the thought that the development of the species is not based on the laws of nature but on freedom. He develops this conclusion primarily out of man and human history. Nietzsche says:

> What surprises me most when surveying the great destinies of man is that I always find the opposite of what Darwin and his followers see or want to see nowadays: selection in favor of the stronger, the better-equipped, the progress of the species. The very opposite is palpably obvious: no consideration of lucky cases, the uselessness of the highly developed types, the unavoidable mastery of the average or even less-than-average types. Assuming that we will not be shown why man is an exception among living creatures, I am inclined to the prejudice that the school of Darwin was wrong everywhere.[9]

> I see all philosophers, I see science kneeling in front of the reality of the very reverse of the struggle for existence, as taught by the school of Darwin. I see that those who win and those who remain are the ones who compromise life and the value of life. The error of Darwin's school became a problem to me. How could they be so blind as to have a wrong view at this point![10]

They count on the struggle for existence, the death of the weak, the survival of the most robust and most highly gifted. Consequently, they imagine a constantly growing perfection for all creatures.

Conversely, however, we have found that, in the struggle for survival, accidents serve the weak as well as the strong, cunning often takes the place of strength to good advantage, and fertility of the species stands in strange relation to the chances of destruction . . .

Both slow and infinite metamorphoses are attributed to natural selection. One tends to believe that advantages are hereditary, and develop ever more strongly in succeeding generations (yet heredity is so capricious!). If you see the felicitous adjustment of certain beings to very special conditions of life, you say that this was achieved by the influence of environment.

But you cannot find examples of unconscious selection anywhere (none at all). The most dissimilar individuals unite, the most extreme ones are mixed with the general mass. Everybody competes to maintain his own type.

. . . There are no intermediate forms.

They claim that there is a growing development of creatures. This has no foundation. Each type has its limits. There is no development beyond them, but up to that point, there is complete regularity.[11]

The most profound reason for the difference between the thinking of Darwin and Nietzsche becomes evident here. Darwin came to his conclusions by an observation of the animal kingdom. From the animal, he transferred them to man and human history. Nietzsche's judgments and observations are primarily oriented toward man and human history. Fundamentally, he commits the same er-

ror of method for which he blames Darwin, only in reverse. From the statement that the laws of Darwin are
not valid for man and for the sphere of history, he draws
the conclusion that "the school of Darwin was wrong
everywhere"—even in the area of the animal kingdom.

By arguing against Darwin, Nietzsche has camouflaged
the fact that his own thinking was strongly influenced by
him. He calls Darwin an example of the "intellect of respectable, but mediocre Englishmen." He is nauseated
by the English "stuffy air of overpopulation that spreads
its breath around Darwinism."

Here the same happens as in many other demonstrable
cases: Nietzsche is deeply stimulated by great thinkers of
his era. But he uses the one point on which he differs
from them to condemn them completely. Thus he
adopts Darwin's idea of development, his theory of descent, and the doctrine of the struggle for survival, but
he transplants both ideas into the sphere of his anthropology, the sphere of freedom. On this basis, he then
blames Darwin for having failed to recognize the sphere
of human freedom. Thus he calls Darwin's doctrine of the
struggle for survival "inconceivably one-sided."[12] In fact,
he raises the indictment of Darwin to an indictment of
the entire English nation. With exorbitant generaliza-
tion, he says: "Darwin has forgotten about the mind.
That's English."[13]

All these are judgments based on the decisive point
from which he has given further development to Darwin's
doctrine. But when he says in his criticism that considering "Darwinism a philosophy"[14] is the "height of confusion," we should not forget how deeply he was influenced
by the philosophical aspect of Darwinism, particularly
in his anthropology and his concept of the superman.
The decisive elements of Nietzsche's superman concept and the specific development of the idealistic genius
concept were supplied by Darwin. In his theory of de-

scent, Darwin showed by the relationship between man and the primates how higher beings with entirely new functions and abilities could emerge in the course of the development of the species, and how the complete line of development aims toward the formation of these higher forms. The new position of the superman, using Nietzsche's terms, can only be conceived on this basis. For him, superman is no longer considered a special form of genius, but as the appearance of a completely new, superior, and higher form of man, entirely different from the type which had previously existed.

No Zarathustra without Darwin! Darwinism and the acceptance of the ideas of evolution and selection into the philosophical and scientific consciousness of the second half of the nineteenth century gave Nietzsche's idea of the superman the halo of scientific probability and made it a myth which could be popularized. It derived its real popularity especially from the operatic sound of the trumpets and fanfares in Nietzsche's own literary presentation and by the theatrical apparel of Zarathustra in the flowing garment of a prophet.

In this criticism of the critics with which we have previously dealt, the real purpose of Nietzsche is quite clearly discernible. This purpose has a number of levels: It still contains the old Christian elements of the superman concept of the early Church, the Christological terms that give his doctrine the character of an anti-Christian Christology, the idealistic impulses, the hero concept of Carlyle, and Darwin's doctrine of evolution. But all these elements were recoined, given a new center, and torn out of their old context. In a polemic way, they are placed into opposition to their own spiritual origin.

However, it would not be proper to condemn Nietzsche because he disavowed those who inspired him. What gives Nietzsche's concept of the superman its own prophetic élan above all previous concepts of "great men," "heroes," "geniuses," and "saints" is the idea that there is an urge in all creatures to reach something which transcends their own personality. This urge has by no means become exhausted or dormant in contemporary man, who also has this transcending urge, an urge of self-realization in a higher form. Here Nietzsche shows consciousness of a development in which hardly any of his contemporaries dared to believe. Here he casts a glimpse into the most profound nature of man which looks forward into the future. Here the old Christian expectation of the end of time comes alive again in its anti-Christian counterpart.

Nietzsche recognizes that the contortions which surround man in the present development of culture and civilization, in fact, the tortures of the "uneasiness about culture," as Sigmund Freud called it later, are nothing but the labor pains of the birth of a greater type of man. For the first time since the days of the long-forgotten mystics of German spiritualism such as Jacob Boehme and Friedrich Christoph Oetinger, Nietzsche develops a progressive anthropology which points to, and is oriented by, the future.

It is only proper to listen to the basic tone of these prophecies, without the polemical asides, without the antitheses rather spasmodically mixed into them, and without the boorish insults:

"I teach you the superman. Man is something that shall be surpassed. What have you done to surpass him?"[15]

"The superman is the meaning of the earth. Let your will say: the superman shall be the meaning of the earth."[16]

"I will teach men the meaning of their existence—the superman, the lightning out of the dark cloud of man."[17]

"Let the radiance of a star shine through your love! Let your hope be: May I give birth to the superman!"[18]

"O my brothers, what I can love in man is that he is a

transition and a destruction. And in you too there is much that lets me love and hope."[19]

"The basic thought: We must take the future as the basis for all our appraisals—and not look behind us to seek for the law of our actions! Not 'humanity' but the superman shall be the goal."[20]

"It is our nature to create a higher being than we are ourselves. To create beyond ourselves! This is the urge of procreation, the urge of action and of work. As all will supposes a purpose, so man supposes a being which does not exist but which is the purpose of his existence. This is the freedom of all will! Love, veneration, longing for perfection are all in the purpose."[21]

Much in these sentences is reminiscent of the formulations of Teilhard de Chardin, especially when he says: "The world is only interesting because of the future" and his idea of *plus-être*, the urge to-be-more which is inherent in existence.[22]

In counterdistinction to the dividing line which Nietzsche draws between himself and Darwinism, we realize here the most profound difference between Nietzsche and Darwin: The superman is not the result of the development of man in terms of a process of natural selection. Nietzsche denies generally that something higher can develop "automatically" out of something lower by a process of selection. But the aim of the future, the last stage of evolution, the superman, is already the condition for the present stage of man and the purpose of man's existence. From the beginning, the superman is the prototype, the inner model for the entire development of life, and has served this purpose since the time present man emerged from the animal kingdom.

The future transition from man to superman was the goal aimed at by the over-all development which led from animal to man and from there to superanimal. All previous stages of evolution exist just for the sake of the superman.

Behind the image of the superman, we see again, albeit in veiled form, the image of the previously existing Son of Man who lived at the beginning of human history. Fallen humanity looked up to him and he was given to humanity, which he accompanied on the entire road of its history. He finally entered and became part of it by becoming man himself. By his resurrection, he initiated the life of the "New Man," the second Adam, and the great transformation of life into the life of the coming age into which all humanity will be drawn and in which the universe shall find its completion.

Nietzsche's perception of the urge in human nature to create something beyond itself, to find self-realization in a higher form, is of truly prophetic character. He has indeed elevated the theory of descent from natural science into the sphere of the spirit and of freedom. He has inquired into the meaning of the total development of life by looking for the goal toward which it was aimed.

But if we expect from Nietzsche an answer to the question of what this higher form of human existence, this coming superhumanity, will look like in concrete terms, we will be greatly disappointed. Just because he gives such prophetic emphasis to the necessity for giving present humanity a higher form, we are disappointed not to get any positive indication as to what these higher, superhuman faculties of humanity may be. He does not speculate about new supramental or parapsychic faculties of the superman.

Actually, the image of the superman, as described by Nietzsche, shows only a definite, strictly limited selection of perfectly normal human qualities. The principle of their selection itself is entirely negative. It is nothing but the elimination of all those qualities which are, in some way, connected with Christian ethics.

This is where the true shortcoming of Nietzsche's superman concept lies. In his critical appraisal of contemporary man, everything is geared to the prophecy of the superman. But when defining the superman himself, all futurism ends. Nietzsche is mainly concerned to draw a line separating the superman in a negative way from the past and the Christian form of man, which prevails at the present time and which is hateful to him. This definition is not accomplished by a description of the new gifts and faculties which Nietzsche expects from the superman, but by the subtraction of all those qualities which he hates particularly in contemporary man because of his specifically anti-Christian emotions. Nietzsche's image of the superman is the antithesis par excellence of the image of contemporary man formed by Christian culture. He wants this antithesis to be as sharply etched as possible.

This negative limitation is expressed most clearly by the fact that Nietzsche connects the appearance of the superman with the death of God, as Dühring did (see above, p. 94). Nietzsche's prophecy about the death of God was the subject of a great deal of guesswork. The solution of the puzzle is that, in both Nietzsche's and Dühring's cases, the idea of the death of God must be understood entirely in the context of Feuerbach's philosophy of religion.

According to Feuerbach, religion is not based on any transcendental reality. Religion and its faith in God or gods is nothing but a mythological self-explanation and self-interpretation of man. In religion, man creates an unreal, imaginary world of the beyond but forgets that this is a world of his own creation. Thus he gets into a slavish state of dependence from his own mythological creations to which he wrongly attributes objective reality.

For Nietzsche the death of God means nothing but the unmasking of the fictitious character of religion and thus the disclosure that the substance of religion can be nobody else but man himself. Up to the present time, man has not seen through the swindle of religion. He is therefore pious, weak, and slavish. He imagines that he depends on a transcendental power but has not yet noticed that he has forged the chains of his own slavery.

The superman, however, is a man who has become aware of the fact that God is dead. He has seen through the swindle of religion and recognizes only himself as the sole center and yardstick of existence.

Therefore the first part of *Thus Spake Zarathustra* concludes quite consistently with the following words:

"Dead are all gods: now we want the superman to live," and

"Let this be our last will on the great noon of the future."[23]

The relation between present and future humanity appears here as the overcoming of a humanity which is still involved in its faith in God by the superman who has freed himself of this faith. Nietzsche proclaims the superman out of the same consideration from which Dühring already derived his demand to turn to the "true man."

For Nietzsche, the death of God is—as it was for Dühring (see above, p. 94)—identical with the collapse of that type of man who has created God and the ethical ideals which are connected with the belief in this God, or, in short, Christian man. To him he attributes nothing but negative qualities such as decadence, weakness, and a negative attitude toward life.

On this basis, the superman appears to be the promethean counterpart of the Christian man, a counterpart which combines all human qualities which Christian ethics would reject. The form of his titanic greatness, and even of his goodness and wisdom, would appear to the present, lower form of man like the Devil incarnate.

"You highest men whom my eyes have seen—this is my

doubt concerning you and my secret laughter: I guess you would call my superman a devil."[24]

Thus Nietzsche's image of the superman is peculiarly unsatisfactory. On the one hand, he conceives it intuitively and foresees it prophetically as the necessary goal of the future development of mankind. He bases it on a critical analysis of the structure of present man, and lifts it as a factor of cultural criticism into the consciousness of his era. On the other hand, the image lacks a precise definition of the proper meaning of the term superman. Nietzsche's so-called superman has only a few human qualities in titanic proportions. They are the qualities which remain when we eliminate all those which are evaluated positively in the Christian catalogue of virtues, and he really strains himself to adorn them with a halo of heroism.

Because of this purely negative fixation of the image of the superman by Nietzsche, the attempt to translate his superman ideal into practice led to the veneration of the beast and thus, in the final analysis, discredited the superman concept.

VIII

*The Christian Expectation of the
End of Time and
the Idea of Technical Progress*

It may seem incredible that technology and technical progress could be connected with Christian expectations of the end of time and the coming of the Kingdom of God. But in actual fact there is an immediate and close connection between Christian ideas of creation and of the Kingdom of God and the development of modern technology. There is also a connection between Christian hope and the technological utopia of the future.

While I was guest professor at universities in Asia, I was repeatedly struck by the observation that, in the various Asian countries, the meeting with, and adjustment to, Western technological civilization occurred in a different manner and with a different speed, depending upon the religious background of the various cultures involved.[1]

In connection with this conclusion, it became clear to me that Western technology is closely connected with the specifically Christian premises of our Western culture. This does in no way imply that the development of technology was only possible on a Christian basis.[2] But we want to emphasize briefly a few viewpoints in which premises of a specifically Christian character emerged in Western technology at the beginning of modern technological development—during the Renaissance, the Reformation, and the Baroque period. Some of these points of view were cited by leading men of the early period of modern technology as the theological reason and justification of their actions.

(1) The first fundamental religious premise of technological activity is the Christian concept of God as the Creator. This statement may appear self-evident or perhaps even trite. Its meaning will become clear, however, when we realize that, for example, Buddhism, one of the great religions, does not know the personalized concept of God at all. Therefore, the idea of God as the Creator is just as unknown to Buddhism as the concept of a created universe given to us by the divine Creator. Significantly, however, Buddhism has not produced a technological culture but has a distinctly anti-technological attitude in many of its schools.

On the other hand, both the Old and the New Testaments connect certain fundamental technological connotations and images with faith in God the Creator. Thus both the Mosaic history of creation and Paul present God as the potter who fashions man out of a lump of clay. This is the image which the prophet Isaiah uses to describe the relationship of man to God and of God to man (45:9).

The other technological image to illustrate God's work as Creator is that of the master builder (Heb. 11:10). God as the architect is also a prototype of technological origin. This image is found in the Old and the New Testaments in many variations and interpretations, and is applied both to the individual as a temple of God, and, particularly, to the "building" of the Church. The idea of creation and the expectation of the end of time are equally determined by this image. In the expectation of the Kingdom of God, God also appears as the master builder of a divine Jerusalem which comes down from heaven, its walls and gates made of diamonds (Rev. 21:12).

The interpretation of God as the great master builder

then finds a characteristic reinterpretation at the time of the awakening of modern natural science, that is, in the early period of the Enlightenment. God is now presented as the great machinist or clockmaker who builds the clock of the world, or the cosmic machine, and keeps it going.[3]

Creation and its maintenance and completion in the Kingdom of God are thus translated into modern technological terms. But this translation does not represent an unjustified or non-sensical transition into a completely strange or new area. It is really a direct continuation of the interpretation of God in the Old and New Testaments as the foreman, technician, potter, master builder, and artist.

(2) The idea of God as Creator of heaven and earth also implies a certain valuation of the world as creation. As creation, the world has, a priori, the character of something temporal and transitory. It is deprived of its divine character, and it is not God. To consider the world as not divine because of the idea of creation is the basis for an entirely new and fearless evaluation of the world by man and of an entirely new and free way of disposing of it. Man considers himself a creature and thus one of the creatures in a world created by God. He faces the world more ingenuously but also with a different degree of responsibility than a man who is convinced of the divinity of the universe and of its various parts.

(3) It is a decisive point that, according to the proclamations in the Old and New Testaments, man has a special position within creation, compared to all other creatures, since he is understood to be the "image of God" (Gen. 1:27, 9:6). This concept, too, has become so self-evident to us that we often fail to properly appreciate the very exceptional character of this interpretation of man.

The idea that man is a creature distinguished from all

others, because God has created him in his image and likeness, has become one of the strongest impulses for man's technological development and realization. For this idea implies that man too, as God's image, has the same faculty of free creativity as God.

(4) Only in this context does Paul's idea that a Christian has the mission to be the fellow workman of God appear in the proper light. It is true that Paul the apostle did not interpret this thought in a primarily technological sense when he wrote to the Corinthians (I Cor. 3:9): "For we are fellow workmen for God; you are God's field, God's building." What he had in mind was rather the building of the community of God on earth and the activity of the apostles as fellow workmen of God in the establishment of his heavenly Kingdom. But it is significant that Paul uses nothing but technological images at the very point where he refers to his apostolic task as the fellow worker of God. Besides the agricultural-technical image of the community as a field, there is the other image of the community as God's building. The fellow worker of God is the apostle who has laid the foundation as a master builder, called and commissioned by God himself (I Cor. 3:10): "According to the commission of God given to me, like a skilled master builder I laid a foundation, and another man is building upon it. Let each man take care how he builds upon it."

The technological connotations of the image cannot be overlooked (I Cor. 3:9). Significantly, the founders of modern technology have felt that the justification of the most far-reaching aims of their technological efforts could be found in this very thought of the destiny of man as *imago dei* and his vocation as the fellow worker of God.

(5) This idea of man as the fellow worker of God has been intensified to the bold proposition that man is called to co-operate with God in the establishment of his Kingdom and to bring the world closer to the divine goal of

creation. By this mandate to be God's fellow worker, the technician and artist feel that they were assigned to positive co-operation with God in the consummation of his Kingdom. In fact, they feel called upon to share God's dominion over the earth.

In this connection, a sentence in the report of creation given in the Old Testament assumes special importance. It is the order God gives man at the end of creation: "And God blessed them, and God said to them: 'Be fruitful and multiply, and fill the earth and subdue it'" (Gen. 1:28).

The great inventors of the beginning period of Western technological development—at the time of the Renaissance, the Reformation, and the early period of the Enlightenment—refer to this order of God to man with ever-increasing emphasis. Even the technicians of today who are estranged from the Christian faith itself and from Christian thinking refer to it. This order was, and still is, understood as a direct vocation of man to co-operate in the work of maintaining and completing creation as a collaborator of God. It is stated unequivocally, in this connection, that technology has the task to co-operate most decisively in the exercise of this joint dominion.[4]

The biblical ideas that have been enumerated are now, in the course of the development of modern technology, appearing with a completely different dynamism and with a different interrelation. In the consciousness of the individual technicians, they were separated to a large extent from their original biblical-Christian justification, but the basic connection with these fundamental biblical premises was never lost entirely. It often appears surprisingly, as an element of inspiration but also of moral apology, at points where such referrals to a religious heritage would not be expected, frequently in the form of a completely secularized utopia of the future of mankind.

Of decisive importance is still a last Christian element upon which modern technology is based and which has a direct connection with the idea of creation, namely, the specifically Christian understanding of time and history. It is true that pre-Christian cultures also had a technology which reached a rather high level in a few cases. But the technology of antiquity lacked the twofold element which became decisive for the unexpected growth of technology in the Christian West: the element of progress and the element of acceleration. Both elements entered into Western thought by way of the Christian expectation of the end of time and of the specifically Christian understanding of time and history.

Christian piety believed that God the Creator was also the Lord of the history of salvation, and that not only the universe, but also human history were directed by a divine plan of salvation. Thus the idea of working toward a final goal and the idea of the progress of world history were implanted into the consciousness of humanity and accelerated human activities.

As we have seen, the Christian consciousness of history is, at the same time, a consciousness that the time has been fulfilled and that this fulfillment begins to work toward its eventual completion. Thus a peculiar, new, and exciting dynamic element enters into the consciousness of time. It is, first of all, the idea of progress. The victory of the Kingdom of God can no longer be delayed. It already occurred in the beginning by Christ's triumph over sin and death. The forces of the Kingdom of God in history can no longer be suppressed. Humanity strives toward *anakephalaiosis*, the co-ordinated organization under one head, namely, Christ (Eph. 1:10).

But this development of the new offspring is no longer a cyclical process. It occurs in a dramatic acceleration directed toward a certain goal, brought about because the struggle between the forces of the old and the new age leads to ever-more-violent blows and counterblows and because this struggle presses by itself toward a final decision.

This acceleration has a particularly far-reaching effect on Christian ethics. For a Christian, the time at his disposal is a limited period, granted to, and measured for, him by God. It is up to him to fill it purposefully, and this purpose is the work for the Kingdom of God.

The calling of fellow worker with God in the completion of creation requires a completely different concept of time which goes far beyond the pre-Christian *Carpe diem*. Time gains a value, hitherto unheard of, as the term during which man has to realize his divine task as God's fellow worker. A Christian also knows that the deadline is set by God and not by himself. This deadline corresponds to a court before which he has to account for his time.

Thus all the actions of a Christian have an eschatological character: "We must work . . . while it is day" (Jn. 9:4), and "Redeem the time" (Eph. 5:16). Both sentences connote the impulse to fill the time with the fulfillment of our divine calling as God's fellow workers. This new concept of time also led to an immeasurable acceleration of technical inventions and of the technological solution of the practical problems of life.

An obvious objection can be raised here: The New Testament passages do not refer at all to activity in the technological sense, but rather to the work and power of the Holy Spirit. Besides, they do not refer to a kingdom of this world, but to the coming Kingdom, which is not of this world.

At first blush, this objection appears to be very justified. But the history of Western Christianity shows that it is not. To be sure, the "work" of man points at first, in its immediate sense, to the charismatic work of the Holy Spirit. But the accelerating and intensifying effect contained in these words manifests itself also in the activity of the faithful in this world and in the area of technology.

It is one of the most amazing facts of Western cultural history that the striking acceleration and intensification of technological development in post-Carolingian Europe emanated from contemplative monasticism, such as the order of the Benedictines and its later reform orders, the Cluniacs and the Cistercians.[5] The basic principle of Benedictine asceticism—*ora et labora*—included daily labor into practical divine service. The time of the monks' "military service" in the order of the heavenly King and under the command of the abbot was divided into liturgical praise of God, meditative Scripture reading, and practical manual labor.

The consciousness that practical manual labor was also done in the service of God and with responsibility to the divine King resulted in all activities in the fields of the *artes mechanicae* and the *artificia* being carried out with the greatest art, application, and punctuality. Thus the time provided by God for this work was filled with a maximum and optimum of value, that is, of technical achievement.

Under the influence of the Benedictine monks of the tenth century, the yield of agriculture in Central Europe was tripled. The number of windmills, watermills, canals, and other installations of artificial irrigation was increased many times. Places of Western mysticism became places of highly developed handicraft and technical science, including the arts of music, painting, and calligraphy. The great mystics of German symbolism, Richard and Hugo of St. Victor, were, at the same time, the great theoreticians of the mechanical arts.[6] In their encyclopedic works, they made the *artes mechanicae* a part of the total substance of human knowledge and understanding. Following St. Augustine, the first Christian theologian of technology,[7] they developed a theology of technical science, considering technology a means to overcome original sin.

A direct projection of "work" for the Kingdom of God into the sphere of practical life and technological activity followed in the sixteenth-century Reformation. During the Reformation, the dualism of the medieval states—the spiritual versus the lay—was overcome by the realization that "spiritual" qualified not an ecclesiastical office but an attitude of faith. All work which is done with faith in God and looking for the coming of his Kingdom is "spiritual" even if it is quite secular and profane. For a pious Christian, work in his profession or trade is divine service and fulfillment of his calling as a fellow worker of God.

Fundamentally, the acceleration of "work," provoked by the Christian consciousness of fulfillment, was thus projected into the sphere of professional work where it had tremendous consequences. It is no accident that, generally speaking, the technological revolution originated among the Protestant nations of England, Germany, Sweden, and later on, North America.[8]

A similar phenomenon can be observed in connection with the latest phase of the technological revolution of nineteenth-century Germany. Late Pietism with its radical orientation toward the other world and the revivalist movement, with its partly chiliastic attitude, of the Rhineland, Westphalia, and Wurttemberg played a great role as an intellectual impulse for industrialization.

The founders of numerous firms which enjoy a wide reputation nowadays were Pietist artisans. By the great sense of responsibility and feeling for quality which they showed in the exercise of their trades, they became successful entrepreneurs. In their enlarged factories, they promoted the economic exploitation of technical inventions, some of which they had made themselves, while others had been made because of their influence.

The Pietist grandfather, who presided over "hours" of

edification, is the ancestor of numerous small and large firms, the shares of which are highly priced today. Their grandchildren own villas in Ticino and most of them have lost the last remnants of their Pietist origin and of the inner-worldly asceticism that goes with it.

In America, too, the development was similar, partly in direct connection with the immigration of German Pietists. The Bethlehem Steel Company in Bethlehem, Pennsylvania, one of the greatest enterprises of the American armament industry, originated in the small smithy of a blacksmith of the Brethren Community who had immigrated from Herrnhut at the beginning of the eighteenth century. He established himself in the Herrnhut mission-settlement of Bethlehem, in the forests of Pennsylvania, where his workshop quickly developed into a large enterprise. The fact that one of America's largest armament factories is called "Bethlehem" indicates its Pietist-pacifist origin to this day.[9]

Thus the acceleration of charismatic work for the Kingdom of God has led, in the course of Western church history, to acceleration, intensification, and a more dynamic form of technological evolution. This was made possible by the connection which does exist within man, as we know from his history, between his faith and the way in which he implements it in life.

The deeper reason for the peculiar and paradoxical connection between Christian understanding of reality, on the one hand, and technological development, on the other hand, lies in the basic idea of Christian religion itself, in the idea of incarnation. The sentence "The word became flesh" involves a concept of reality which is the very opposite of any dualism of spirit and flesh or of spirit and matter.

No one less than the Anglican Archbishop William Temple has expressed this thought in a boldly pointed way. In an address, which has since become famous, the

Archbishop asked the International Conference of Missions held in Jerusalem in 1928 how the non-Christian religions would deal with Western civilization and technology now breaking into their area. This subject has since assumed even more urgently topical character by the tremendous progress of technology in Asia and Africa and by the measures of development aid.

In this connection, Temple pointed to the Christian roots of Western technology. With great clarity, he expressed the thought that, basically, an intelligent domination and responsible handling of technology was only possible by the spiritual premises from which technology had grown:

> What is the Hindu reformer to do with steam and electricity? His religion says they are part of the illusion of life; it will not help him to control them. He may try to neglect them, as Mr. Gandhi does, but they will be too strong for him . . . What is wanted is a religion for which matter is the proper vehicle of spirit, and spirit is recognized to act by directing matter; and Christianity alone answers to that description. Its central affirmation is that "the Word was made flesh." It is the most materialistic of all higher religions, for while they attain to spirituality by turning away from matter, it expresses its spirituality by dominating matter . . . For Christianity, matter exists to be the vehicle of spirit, and is only fulfilling its true function when it is that; but spirit realizes itself by controlling matter and only expresses itself so far as it does that. Taught by the Incarnation, the Christian finds all the universe a sacrament, which finds its focal expression in the Word made flesh.[10]

By its very nature, technology, in a peculiar way, helps men's striving toward the future and perfection. In art, philosophy, and religion, knowledge which characterized an entire era is forgotten again and again. But it is different in technology. There, inventions remain and spread until they are replaced by better ones. "There are no final achievements in art, upon which all subsequent periods will build, as in technology, where new inventions can always accumulate on the tremendous base of the development of a hundred thousand years." The development of technology is irreversible. Even catastrophes and their reverses cannot change this.[11]

Philosophers and theologians have paid too little attention to this unique phenomenon of steadiness and progression in technical development and to its inherent tendency for integration, universality, and catholicity as distinct from the dialectical aimlessness and particularity in other fields of the human spirit.

Teilhard de Chardin has pointed out this side of technology.[12] Modern technology is indeed the only human creation which has attained global universality. The catholicity of technology is more all-embracing than the catholicity of the Catholic Church and more ecumenical than the Ecumenical movement.

The modern technological revolution has never been able to deny its eschatological roots, its determination by a Christian understanding of time and history. It converted the Christian expectation of the coming of the Kingdom of God into a technological utopia. It is determined that its technologically interpreted kingdom be "taken by force" or be "entered violently" (Mt. 11:12, Lk. 16:6).

The oldest technological utopias are in their entirety still portions of Christian utopias. The image of perfection at the end of time and of the Christian promise of salvation is represented by a perfect society in a city on a remote island or in a state of a distant continent. Examples are Thomas More's *Utopia* (1515), Thomas Campanella's "Sun State"—*Civitas Solis*—of 1602, the *Nova*

Solyma of Samuel Golt (1648), the *Christianopolis* of
Johann Valentin Andreae (1619), and the *New Atlantis*
by Francis Bacon (1625).

In the case of Francis Bacon, the connection between
technological utopia and Christian eschatology is still pal-
pably obvious. In his image of New Atlantis, he describes
an ideal state, representing conditions in the Kingdom of
God. Spiritual knowledge is presented as the highest degree of scientific knowledge. Christian virtues are realized
by a technical domination of nature, which already fore-
shadows all modern technological inventions by its utopian descriptions. The technical aspect of these older
Christian utopias can still arouse the enthusiasm of modern technicians. L. Mumford, the well-known city planner, speaks with utmost admiration about Johann Valentin Andreae's *Christianopolis* (Strasbourg, 1619). He
describes it as the ideal model for a modern city.[13]

The terminological difference between utopia and eschatology is difficult to establish. It has been pointed out
that the voluntary element in the modern utopia, expressed by pedagogical idealism and the consciousness of
social responsibility, makes it easier to distinguish it from
eschatology.[14] But, as we have shown previously, the
early Church was already familiar with the voluntary element of taking a direct influence upon the acceleration of
the coming of the final Kingdom, not to mention the
radical pedagogical idealism of eschatological asceticism.
It is probably wrong altogether to compare utopia and
eschatology on the same chronological level. Utopia is the
modern form of eschatology. It corresponds to an advanced stage of the Christian consciousness of history in
which the "fellow worker" for the Kingdom of God has
become a "fellow planner."

Direct aftereffects of the early Christian eschatology
can be traced to the social utopias of the nineteenth century. They are still particularly evident in Saint-Simon's

social utopia, the *Nouveau Christianisme* of 1825. Here, the coming industrial state is described and characterized by a strictly hierarchical organization of industrial functions, modeled on church hierarchy. The intellectual authority held by clerics in the Middle Ages will be assigned to researchers and scholars, and the organized industrial state will be a "Church of Intelligence." A social highpriest, a kind of industrial pope, will be at the top, and it will be led by a spirit of a reasonable Christianity.[15]

This eschatological feature remained with modern technological development throughout all phases of the technological revolution. If you read modern literature about the ideological basis of technology, you will be surprised to find how strongly technical utopians are influenced by ethical and idealistic motives. This is particularly true of literature written by technicians and inventors and not by philosophers and theologians whose sole connection with technical matters is their license to drive an automobile.

Instead of many others, we will only mention David Friedrich Strauss who is generally known only as the founder of radical historical New Testament criticism and as the author of *Leben Jesu* (American edition: *The Life of Christ*, New York: Vale, 1845). As his book *Der alte und der neue Glaube* shows, the same David Friedrich Strauss was also an enthusiastic protagonist of the technological revolution. He transposed the Christian expectation of the end of time into an idea of technological progress, and was one of the first to recognize and announce the tremendous progress which would follow the invention of the steam engine, resulting in power that could be generated by a technical method and that could be used for various tasks, thereby setting different kinds of other machines into motion. This would be the beginning of a unique liberation of man. He writes:

Man can and should not only understand nature, but also dominate it. This applies both to external nature, as far as his powers admit, and to the natural within him. Here again a very important and rich field of human endeavor finds the recognition and the consecration denied it by Christianity. Not only the inventor of printing—since his invention furthered the dissemination of the Bible—but those, too, who taught the steam engine to fly along iron rails, thought and speech to flash along the electric wire— works of the Devil, according to the consistent view of our pietists—are from our standpoint fellow worker in the Kingdom of God. Technology and industry may further luxury, which by the way is a relative term, but they also further humanity.[16]

The new image of man, formed by the technological revolution, is also dominated entirely by eschatological features. The "new man" is the master of the elements who has been chosen to hold sovereign sway over nature. Of special significance for this development are spontaneous remarks of contemporaries who participated, full of wonder, in the first spectacular manifestations of technological progress.

The following is a description of the inauguration of the railroad line from Nuremberg to Fürth, the first one built in Germany, on December 7, 1835. It was given by an unnamed reporter of the *Stuttgarter Morgenblatt* and describes the locomotive engineer as an ideal image of the "New Man" of the technological revolution. In this description, we find a number of mythological and eschatological images.[17]

Besides, we were equally absorbed by the quiet, circumspect and confidence-instilling behavior of the English charioteer. Who would not see in such a man the personification of the entire difference between

modern times and the old and intermediate periods!
Any physical dexterity, which still is important too,
becomes secondary and merely serves the reasonable
attention even to the smallest detail as an important
part of the whole. Each shovel of coal which he puts
in involves consideration of the right measure, the
right time, and the right distribution on the hearth.
Not idle for a moment, watching everything, figuring
out the minute at which he has to set the car into
motion, he appeared to be the ruling spirit of the
machine, and of the elements combined in it, for a
tremendous power-effect . . .

Gradually, the charioteer allowed the force of the
steam to become effective. Clouds of steam push out
of the smokestack in tremendous thrusts, which can
be compared to the panting of a gigantic antedilu-
vian bull . . . The panting and the smoke of the es-
caping steam, which is lifted up as a cloud, do not
fail to have an effect. Horses on the nearby highway
bolted at the approach of the monster, children wept
and people who cannot be called uneducated were
unable to suppress a slight trepidation. Unless a person has no imagination at all, he cannot remain quiet
and without amazement when first looking at this
wondrous phenomenon.

But this amazement is then followed by a comfort-
ing feeling caused by reflection. It is the feeling that
the forces of the human mind and of human invention have triumphed over the elements which, as
Schiller so aptly remarked, "hate what has been created by human hands." How strange! Such an uplifting feeling wells up when you look at the hundreds and thousands who hardly have an idea how
much knowledge and experience, how many experi-
ments and combinations, how much ingenuity, genius, and good luck have to be combined to invent and

construct such a machine. For them, all this is a miracle in which they believe, because they saw it. No
esoteric skeptic will be able to shatter our new belief
in the human spirit and its power, particularly not,
because it is so joyful and uplifting.

The technological myth of the "New Man" reflects the
undeniable fact that, with the development of technology, there is a parallel development of human consciousness. Indeed, it appears that the two developments are
identical.

The development of human self-consciousness, on the
other hand, is identical with the development of human
freedom. The history of human technology, which covers
hundreds of thousands of years, is closely linked with the
history of human freedom.

In his work *Die Technik als Kulturmacht in sozialer
und geistiger Beziehung* published in Berlin in 1906, Ul-
rich Wendt has very aptly outlined the historical development of technology in various eras in terms of the degree
to which the intellectual character of human labor and
thus the "process of liberation" increased progressively.

These various degrees cannot be described here in detail. Suffice it to refer briefly to the last two. As David
Friedrich Strauss remarked correctly, the last and decisive
step into freedom was taken through the machine. It
made it possible to generate power and to have mechanical performances carried out by other machines.

In the background of the enthusiastic praise of the
steam engine, which we quoted above, is the realization
that the steam engine initiated the abolition of the classic
form of slavery. There is a direct inner connection between industrial revolution and social revolution. The
control over the machine and the capacity to produce and
apply power to a previously unimaginable extent have
lifted humanity to a new level of self-consciousness and

freedom. In his book *Voyage en Icarie*, published in 1839, the social utopian Etienne Cabet extols the steam engine as the truly revolutionary power of the coming century. "The modest fire and the simple water will blast aristocracy into the air and smash it into the ground. There are still the old four elements, but steam is a fifth one and not less important than the others, for it creates the world of the future and separates our present time from the past."

The phase of the power-producing machine in which electricity, oil, and atomic power came to the fore beside steam power, has meanwhile been made obsolete by the phase of automation and cybernetics into which we have entered.

At first, the machine forced its own rhythm upon man in the labor process, a feature which was very convincingly caricatured by Charlie Chaplin. But increasingly, automation assigns the various phases of production to the machine itself and makes man independent of its own rhythm of work. The tendency is instead that man's share be concentrated more and more upon the functions of planning, directing, and controlling which undoubtedly means a higher degree of freedom.

The further reduction of working time in this phase, and the resulting increase of "free" leisure time, has also made a new and significant contribution toward the development of freedom. It should not be said that this progress only concerns the "material freedom" of man. After all, material freedom always was the basis of man's spiritual freedom.

The idea of technological development leads inescapably to the question as to when the technological age will end. Among the current widespread concepts of the end of the technological age, we find various types of Christian expectations of the end of time projected into the world of technology.

The first type is suggested by the pessimists among the critics of technological civilization. They expect that the world will be destroyed by the abuse of technology. Interpreted in technological terms, this is the great explosion, the supreme "bang." Using its maximal potential of destruction which it has reached by the control of atomic energy, humanity of the technological age will blow itself up. Optimists like Teilhard de Chardin do not entirely exclude such an end, but they do not consider it likely since it would contradict the general idea of a meaningful evolution of life.

The second type of concept of the end of the technological age was developed in the modern morphology of culture. It is the idea of the self-exhaustion of technology. Tied up to a certain form of culture, it will become extinct with that culture. Oswald Spengler, for instance, declares that the technological revolution is a typical expression of the Faustian culture of the nordic race, while for the colored people (according to Spengler, the Russians belong to this category), Faustian technology does not fill an inner need.[18] According to him, technology will therefore perish with the nordic race that created it.

If we keep in mind the extent to which technology has become a matter for humanity as a whole during the last two decades, how much it has contributed to unify humanity, and what a positive contribution the Russians in particular have made toward it, we can only express amazement at such fallacious diagnosis.

The arguments given by Georg Siebers in 1963 in his work *Das Ende des technischen Zeitalters* are more serious. He points out that with the discovery of atomic energy, technology has reached its end. "The discoveries of Göttingen and Peenemünde play the funeral march and not the prelude of the technological age."[19] Siebers also argues that the technique of communication has reached a potential which enables humanity to participate in important historical events while they happen. It has thus reached the absolute limit.[20] By its nature, the technique of communication cannot very well be expected to offer humanity more news transmission through words or pictures than, for example, the election of a pope or the assassination of a president. To expect a television set to show tomorrow's events today would be asking too much.

Such considerations come from philosophers. They reflect quite an understandable cultural pessimism which actually is not fed by a criticism of technology itself, but rather by its present forms of industrialization and commercialization.[21]

If we talk to high-caliber scientists and technicians we find that matters look completely different. Do we really control the atom? The experts say that we still stand at the beginning of atomic technology. It is impossible to predict the end of this development. More areas of understanding for the structure of matter open up all the time and thus more chances for its technical exploitation. Besides, we can well imagine that completely new technological developments may occur and are, in fact, already prepared in different areas. In this connection, we think, for instance, of those scientists who try to bypass the development of the combustion engine and of atomic technology by so-called "cold combustion." This would eliminate the entire present phase of noisy and smelly combustion engines which poison the atmosphere of cities. It would also eliminate unprofitable atomic reactors with their dangerous atomic waste as sources of energy.[22] A technological invention in the field of the conservation and transformation of solar energy or cosmic rays could bring about, in a short period of time, a complete change in the present forms of our culture. It could remove many of the negative features connected with our present methods of technical production which our critics of culture find so upsetting.

The universalism inherent in the character of technology and its roots in human striving toward perfection rather point in a third direction, namely, to a Joachimitism projected into the sphere of a technological world and endeavoring to give technology an increasingly spiritual character.

The idea of the end of the technological age, as interpreted by Siebers, is thus questionable. It proceeds from the assumption that an extroverted, materialistic and technological civilization could be succeeded by an introverted culture which turns its attention back to man's inner life. This dualism is based on wrong premises. Technology is not "materialistic" because it deals with the formation of matter; it is a unique achievement of the human spirit by which man progressively gives concrete corporeal expression to his inner world and which is intimately linked with human consciousness and human freedom. Technology is the extension of the body of universal man by which he realizes his spiritual universality in concrete terms.

Humanity will continue to perfect its technological body to extend the boundaries of its material freedom and to widen the area of the second creation until it has given corporeal expression to the *imago dei*, the imprint of which it bears.

This poses the problem of a Christian theology of technology for our time. Nowadays most theologians do nothing more than declare that technology is something "demonic." This means, in effect, that they leave technology, and the world which it created, to the Devil.

This thesis is questionable, if only for the reason that those theologians who frowningly endorse it, use the technical comforts of our time quite innocently and extensively. But considering the total share which technology had for hundreds of thousands of years in the development of humanity and human consciousness, it would be more important to ask the following question: Does technology form part of the history of salvation and, if so, in what sense? Is it, as Augustine taught, an expedient, a crutch, given man to make his life easier despite original sin, or is it itself, as Hugo of St. Victor claimed, a remedy against original sin? Is it, as Teilhard de Chardin explained, the springboard of man's evolution into the superhuman?

In a time like ours, in which the technological progress of human life has reached such a high level and in which man uses technology to give direction to his own evolution, the time has come for theologians to rediscover the eschatological perspective of hope in this central area of anthropology and to work out a proper theology of technology adapted to our times.

IX

The Christian Interpretation of the Theory of Evolution in Anglo-Saxon Theology

In European religious and intellectual history, little attention was given to nineteenth-century American theology. Up to this day, two prejudices are cultivated in Europe in relation to the American religious and intellectual history of that period, and even intensive co-operation at meetings of the World Council of Churches between European and American theologians has hardly succeeded in reducing these preconceived opinions. The first prejudice is: *Americana non leguntur*—"one does not read American literature," in this case, theological literature. The second prejudice is: "There is no independent American theology."

Both prejudices have led to considerable damage to European intellectual history, for both of them are wrong. The first cannot be repaired, for the time being. There is no library in all of Germany in which more than exceptional fragments of American nineteenth-century theological literature are available. The claim that there is no separate American theology has helped to cultivate theological arrogance in Europe. In this ecumenical age, this has proven to be a provincialism which can hardly be excused.

This ignorance about American theology has also led to the recent fashion of overrating Teilhard de Chardin. His Christian interpretation of evolution and its application to Christian anthropology and eschatology are neither as new nor as unique as they are reputed to be.

Theological confrontation with the natural sciences occurred in American Protestant theology in a much more dynamic and less prejudiced way fifty years earlier than in Europe. This applies particularly to the theory of evolution in biology, anthropology, and even paleoanthropology. While European Protestant theology was mainly occupied with questions of historical criticism of the New Testament and church history, North American and to a certain extent English theology had as its central theme the discussion of the findings of modern natural science. Ever since the publication of Darwin's main work, this applies particularly to the theory of evolution.

The theological discussion within the Anglo-Saxon countries differed in style and method from the continental European one, and particularly from that conducted within German theology. There were two distinctive criteria. First, the discussion was conducted by a category of scholars which did not exist in Europe, or at least not for a century until Teilhard de Chardin again brought it to the fore. We are referring to theologians who were simultaneously prominent scholars in at least *one* area of natural science. Some of them were scientists and clergymen at the same time. Out of inner compulsions generated by their scientific knowledge and the understanding of their faith, they looked for the establishment of a meaningful relationship between the two areas, namely, of their experience and their understanding.

Secondly, it must be noted that the discussion in the Anglo-Saxon countries not only took the form of learned scientific or theological treatises, but also had a strongly journalistic character. The participating scientific clergymen or clerical scientists submitted their findings to their congregations in topical sermons or addresses, and their theses were made the subject of a lively, broad and public discussion. Some of them were men of great literary ability. They were editors of progressive Christian periodicals and explained their evolutionist interpretations of Christian anthropology and eschatology to a broad public in widely read articles. Thus a wide discussion was indeed initiated in the fields of theology and natural science, a phenomenon for which there is hardly a parallel in Germany.

It is only fitting today, to look at the Anglo-Saxon forerunners of Teilhard de Chardin after analogous problems were recognized, rather belatedly, and perhaps somewhat after the event, by European theology. They all radiate nineteenth-century optimism which is taboo nowadays. But, in view of the general *Bonjour tristesse* mood cultivated by contemporary European theology under the influence of existentialism, it cannot do any harm to realize that there is also a vigorous tradition of Christian optimism. Teilhard de Chardin's optimism, which is exposed to so many attacks nowadays, has respectable ancestors.[1]

One of the earliest theological confrontations with the idea of evolution goes back to the American theologian Minot Judson Savage (1841–1918).[2] He was, at first, a Congregationalist and supporter of a traditional conservative biblicism, a fundamentalist. He was a missionary during the wild times of expansion to the West and of the gold rush in California. He soon began to look critically at his own theological position and later turned to the Unitarian Church. Successively, he was elected preacher at three of the most important Unitarian churches in the United States, first in Chicago, then at the Church of the Unity in Boston, and finally at the Church of the Messiah in New York City.

There is no doubt that there had been a theological analysis of Darwinism before him. Because of his popularity and reputation as a clergyman, Savage was the first American preacher who could afford to draw the attention of American Protestantism, particularly of its clergy, very forcefully to the necessity of a confrontation with the doctrine of evolution. After decades of a shocklike, ferocious rejection of Darwinism which was particularly propagated by fundamentalist circles, Savage became the trailblazer of a positive Christian appreciation of the results of modern natural science.

Savage turned very forcefully against the opinion, generally widespread in Christian circles, that the theory of evolution "is driving God clear out of his universe."[3] He proved that, on the contrary, it is the idea of evolution which leads to a true understanding of the biblical idea of creation. It is the idea of evolution which makes it possible to find in the entire universe, in all the various degrees in which it has attained concrete form, "the footprints of God."

> And so, anywhere where God has been, or where God is now (for he is now where he ever has been), wherever God is, I look upon his very footsteps, and I can put my finger into his own finger-prints; and I can see God's life in the growth and progress of nature about me; I can feel the divine pulsations in the air, and in the life of my body; I am living in the midst of the only temple that God himself has consecrated, and that I can be absolutely sure is a representation of God's own work. Whether there are mistakes about any thing else or not, this is certain. Here, then, in nature—in sun and star, and sky and cloud, and ocean and earth, and grass and flowers and trees, and human nature—I am looking directly into a revelation of God; and if I can read it, I can read the very thoughts and processes and methods of the divine working and development.[4]

The doctrine of evolution can help man to advance to "a grander God, a nobler humanity, a more magnificent universe as the theatre for human action."[5] In a manner similar to that of Teilhard de Chardin, where the God of evolution is boldly called "more magnificent than Jehovah," Savage calls the God of evolution the *"grander God."*

Savage also expressed the thought that the unity and continuity of the evolution of life leads to the conclusion that there is already a preliminary form of life in matter. "Science . . . does not believe any matter is dead: so it finds in it 'the promise and potency of every form of life.' . . . This little mass, or cell, is not the lowest and most original form of life, but it is the basis of every form. There is no single form of life on the globe, from the moss on a stone up to the brain of Sir Isaac Newton, that is not a more or less complex compound or combination of this primary, tiny cell . . ."[6]

There is a continuous chain of life which reaches from the first signs of life within matter itself to the most complicated form of the organization of matter, as represented by the human brain. It is a chain which reaches "from the moss on a stone to the brain of Sir Isaac Newton."

As this quotation indicates, Savage—as did Teilhard de Chardin later on—concludes from the evolution of the brain that man represents the culmination of the cosmic process of evolution. Cerebration appears to be the axle of evolution. Savage writes about this as follows: "The natural force of development worked on the body until it reached its upright attitude and present comparative perfection. Then, when brain-power became the winning element in the struggle for life, the same force turned to brain. And now the moral is gradually gaining supremacy; and the time will come when this will be reckoned the mightiest, as it is now admitted to be the noblest, force of humanity. The moral power is coming to be the power that wins."[7] This thesis made his biographer, C. H. Lyttle, refer to Savage's powerful optimistic emphasis upon human progress.[8]

This revelation of God attaining through evolution the highest form of the organization of matter in the human brain has not yet reached its final form in present-day man. It still strives toward a higher type of man.

"Thus the panorama of creation has unfolded. The first scene was the fire-mist: the last that we have looked on is the present hour, including the highest social, political, and religious life and aspirations of the race. And the end is not yet: the creation is not still: the scene is moving and unfolding to-day. And if we may guess the future from the past, the imagination must confess that it has no colors bright and grand enough to paint the possibilities of the ages to come."[9]

"The God of evolution," Savage continues, "the hidden life and secret force of this unfolding universe of ours, drives the development of humanity on to higher degrees of human existence. Above the common level of our humanity there rise the exceptional and towering summits of those mountainous men—seers, prophets, poets, law-givers, leaders of every kind—that have served as landmarks and observatories for the race."[10] And Savage concludes his observations as follows: "If such men spring out of humanity, it is because there is in humanity the stuff of which such men are made . . . And thus the fact that the race is seen on its face, adoring the idealized forms of these sublime and divine men, is proof that humanity is potentially such as they."[11]

For those who observe the development of life in its totality, the doctrine of evolution makes it possible to recognize the final rank of man within this development and, in fact, impresses it upon them. The doctrine of evolution suggests that "all life on the globe is a unit, like a tree, and man is the crowning blossom on the topmost bough."[12]

To put man into the proper order of the animalistic preliminary steps of evolution does not imply a devaluation of, but rather hope for, future perfection. "I am not half as anxious to find out that I did not come from an ape, as I am to know that I am not travelling toward one. Where we came from touches not the matter of what we are. 'Now are we the sons of God' [I Jn. 3:1]; and if evolution be true, well and grandly we may add, 'It doth not yet appear what we shall be' [I Jn. 3:2]. People who get up in the world are sometimes ashamed of their parentage; but I think it much more important that we be careful that our children have no reason to be ashamed of their parentage. And since my line runs back millions of years, and ends in God, I see no good cause for being ashamed of the long and wondrous way by which it has come."[13]

As in the case of Teilhard de Chardin, the God of evolution himself appears to be the origin and goal of evolution. In putting man in his proper place on the scale of the evolution of previous forms of life, Savage has, however, made a slight adjustment of borderlines among the higher mammals and particularly among the primates. In this manner, he apparently hoped to exonerate the doctrine of evolution in relation to the traditional prejudices of Christian anthropology.

For traditional Christian thinking, the objectionable point was man's descent from the ape because it appeared that this point obliterated the borderline between man and animal and abandoned the unique, special position of man. Savage has thus placed the critical point of evolution within the evolution of man himself. He expressed the thought that "The gulf that separates the highest animals from the lowest men is as nothing compared with the wider differences that divide between those lowest men and the Dantes, the Shakspered, and the Newtons of the race."[14]

The idea that the highest form of our human species is further distant from the lowest one than the latter is from the highest form of animal is an apologetic attempt to make the jump from animal to man look harmless. But it carries within itself the dangerous possibility of drawing a dividing line through humanity itself and base it upon an ideologically determined anthropology. Whatever lies below the dividing line, on the allegedly subhuman level, is pushed back into the animal kingdom.

The same thought which Savage expresses as part of his general progress-optimism reminds us of similar statements made much more recently. "The differences among the various races can sometimes be enormous, both externally and thus, obviously, also internally. And they are indeed. The margin between the lowest so-called men and other, highest races is wider than that between the lowest men and the highest types of apes." These words are found in H. Brücher's book *Ernst Haeckels Bluts- und Geisteserbe.*[15] But they are only given as a quotation from an address delivered by Adolf Hitler at the Reich Party Rally in Nuremberg (1935) which preceded the proclamation of the Nuremberg Laws.

Similar thoughts have also been expressed by older German Darwinists, for example, by A. Ploetz in *Über die Tüchtigkeit unserer Rasse und den Schutz der Schwachen, ein Versuch über Rassenhygiene und ihr Verhältnis zu den humanen Idealen, besonders zum Sozialismus.* He claims that the level of the so-called "lower" or "primitive" races, including the Negroes, is as far below that of the whites as the level of a gorilla is below that of a Negro.[16]

In a similar manner, A. Tille, author of the book *Von Darwin bis Nietzsche* (Leipzig, 1895), claims that the Dravidas and pygmies of inner Africa "are not human beings in our sense of the word."[17]

In a highly instructive essay, entitled "Darwinismus und Zeitgeist," Fritz Bolle has pointed out this problem of introducing ideological criteria into the evaluation of man's evolution.[18] However, it escaped Bolle's attention that it was Ernst Haeckel who first formulated this thought.

The psychological differences between men and the anthropoid apes are smaller than the corresponding differences between the anthropoid apes and the lowest types of monkeys. This psychological fact corresponds exactly with the anatomical findings shown by the difference in the construction of the meninges of the cerebrum, the most important "soul organ." The great importance of these findings becomes even clearer if we keep in mind how much men differ in their emotional lives. High above, we see a Goethe and Shakespeare, a Darwin and Lamarck, a Spinoza and Aristotle. Compare them, far below, with a Vedda and Akka, an Australian aborigine and Dravida, a Bushman and Patagonian! The tremendous interval between the emotional lives of those highest and lowest representatives of the human species is much wider than that between the latter and the anthropoid apes.[19]

The doctrine of evolution has the tendency to dissolve the borderline between animal and man into a multitude of transitional stages which are distributed over periods of hundreds of thousands of years. In case of an ideological interpretation, this stretching of the borderline makes it tempting to use the long scale to move the borderline up or down according to ideological criteria of value. The line is thus transferred into the area of *homo sapiens* himself and connected with a racial theory. Depending upon ideological, political or social circumstances, sometimes one or the other race remains below the borderline which has been declared authoritative. The logic of this thought does not cause any scruples to the followers of a materialistic ideology. But Savage was a convinced Christian. He was hardly aware of the catastrophic political consequences of his thesis.

But a problem emerges in the works of Savage which we will find again in the case of Teilhard de Chardin. It is used by the orthodox side to organize resistance against him. In view of the interpretation of the history of salvation as a history of evolution toward a higher type of man, the traditional orthodox doctrine of original sin cannot be maintained any longer. As Leibniz did under similar circumstances, evil is reduced, in the final analysis, to the *malum metaphysicum*. It belongs to the present state of the world, but its purpose is to contribute toward the progress of evolution. Evil is a symptom of an evolution which has not been completed yet. On the other hand, it is a necessary element to keep evolution going.

"Evil," says Savage, "is simply a temporary and passing condition. To put the whole thing in one word, all evil is nothing more or less than maladjustment. The devil, and sin, and sorrow, and calamity, and sickness, and tears, and death, all resolve themselves into this one word."[20] And with that radical unconcern which Teilhard can no longer afford, Savage continues: "The devil is a dream of the night and darkness of the past. Let him be relegated to the museum of theological curiosities, mummies, and skeletons, that the coming ages will study to find out the world's thoughts that have passed away."[21]

For the Unitarian, the history of salvation is, in the final analysis, identical with the history of humanity, and the perfection of Christianity is identical with the perfection of humanity. "The underlying principles of Christianity, and the underlying principles of humanity, as it moves on toward perfection, are perfectly identical."[22]

Later on, Teilhard uses the term "supernatural" only with some hesitation because, from the standpoint of evolution, the so-called supernatural is only a higher degree of nature which has developed out of previous stages of evolution. In a similar manner, Savage does not want to apply the term "supernatural" to these highest degrees. "What is that principle? This: All the myriad forms, forces, movements, and life of the universe, are only the varied manifestation of the divine life that lives in the works through it all. The divisions between natural and supernatural, sacred and secular, are broken down."[23]

Almost in the same sense, Teilhard de Chardin refers to the "sacred earth." Without knowing F. C. Oetinger, the American theologian develops here a *theologia ex idea vitae deducta.*

The efforts toward a theological understanding of evolution were then continued by James McCosh (1811–94).[24] He was a Scot by birth. He studied theology at the universities of Glasgow and Edinburgh and was brought up entirely in the spirit of conservative Scotch Presbyterianism. He became a co-founder of the Free Church of Scotland which had seceded from the Scottish state church because it rejected the state-church system and the financial and political dependence of the Church which resulted from it. From 1852–68 he was professor of philosophy at Queens College, Belfast. Then, in 1868 he received a call to serve as president of the College of New Jersey at Princeton, where he taught until his death.

His principal works dealing with the relationship between Christianity and modern natural science are: *Christianity and Positivism* (1871), and especially *The Religious Aspect of Evolution* (1890), a book which was published in New York and exercised a great influence upon American intellectual life.

McCosh takes a most vigorous stand against the attitude, widespread among American clergymen, to denounce the doctrine of evolution founded by scholars like Darwin, Lewes, Huxley, and Spencer as atheism, and to declare it unacceptable to a Christian. He says: "I felt it to be my only course not to reject the truth because it was proclaimed by some who turned it to an irreligious use, but to accept it wherever it might lead, and to turn it to a better use."[25]

In his opinion, this discrimination against the doctrine of evolution, customary in his time, and repeated from most pulpits, in church periodicals, and seminaries would have only negative results. Youth, searching for knowledge, would be driven into skepticism. The findings of natural science prove to young people that evolution is a fact which dominates the entire life of the universe. But, on the other hand, the Church teaches that you cannot be a Christian and support evolution at the same time. In most cases, the result is that people turn away from the Church.

The main purpose of his book *The Religious Aspect of Evolution* is to prove that God expresses himself in nature through evolution, and that acceptance of the scientifically proved fact of evolution can very well be reconciled with the Christian understanding of creation, man, and the universe. Indeed, he points out that some Christian ideas and hopes received a new meaning because of evolution. Until then, they seemed to be hanging in air as paradoxes and their clash with the modern scientific way of looking at the world was always pointed out.

This applies particularly to the Christian expectation of the end of time. Referring to the "coming time," McCosh writes: "In all the geological ages we find in any one age the anticipation of the following. This may also be the case with the age in which we now live, the Age of Man. We see everywhere preparations made for further progress: seeds sown which have not yet sprung up; embryos not yet developed; life which has not yet grown to maturity. In particular we find that in this Age of Man, man has not yet completed his work."[26]

The urge to reach a higher stage, inherent in life on all levels, is also effective on the highest level hitherto reached, that of man. This urge beyond oneself, is the urge for improvement and perfection: "Nature is struggling, but it is in order to improvement. It is ploughing and sowing, but in order to reap in due season. It is moving onward, but also upward. It is groaning, but it is to be delivered from a load. It is travailing, but it is for a birth. It is not perfect, but it is going on toward perfection."[27]

The events of the history of salvation in the Christian era are also understood as being the last links of this chain of perfection of life. Both the genesis of man and the coming of the Holy Ghost are not unique irruptions into history or a breakthrough of masses of lava from the depth, which subsequently harden and remain as blocks of stone. They rather represent the opening of a new stage of human existence, a new phase of perfection of man, so that man and God will eventually converge.

> In all past ages there have been new powers added. Life seized the mineral mass, and formed the plant; sensation imparted to the plant made the animal; instinct has preserved the life and elevated it; intelligence has turned the animal into man; morality has raised the intelligence to love and law. The work of the Spirit is not an anomaly. It is one of a series; the last and the highest. It is the grandest of all the powers. It is an inward power, convincing, converting, sanctifying, beautifying, and preparing the soul for a heavenly rest, where, however, "they rest not day nor night" [Rev. 4:8]; for rest consists in holy and blessed service.[28]

McCosh uses the words of the Gospel of John and of the first letter to the Corinthians to describe the goal of this evolution, toward which the coming of the Holy Spirit leads the last phase of the development of humanity: "And the Word became flesh and dwelt among us"

(Jn. 1:14). Creator and creation are brought into a close relationship to each other.

But the goal which should be reached through the kingdom of godly man has now been attained: " 'When all things shall be subdued unto him, then shall the Son also himself be subject unto him that put all things under him, that God may be all in all' (I Cor. 15:28). I can see no farther into the endless light that stretches out beyond. My hope is to be there and live there forever; then shall I know, even as also I am known."[29] At this point, we should note that the quotation from I Corinthians 15:28—"that God may be all in all"—is the same one to which Teilhard de Chardin refers whenever he demonstrates his idea of the convergence of the evolution of the universe in point Omega.

Henry Drummond (1851–97) is possibly the most important among the Anglo-Saxon theologians of evolution. He is, at the same time, the only Anglo-Saxon theologian of evolution who had a certain, albeit moderate, effect on the continent of Europe. In Germany, he became known through the translation of his main works.[30] He studied natural science in Tübingen, and in the fall of 1873, he became involved in the revivalist movement which emanated from the famous American revivalist preacher Dwight L. Moody. From April 1874 to July 1875, he traveled with Moody, working with him in his revivalist work. In particular, he helped him in his personal ministration in the famous "inquiry-room" in which Moody dealt with the personal problems of those of his listeners who had been deeply stirred by his sermons.

In 1879, Henry Drummond undertook a geological expedition to the Rocky Mountains. In 1883, he went on a journey of exploration to Africa. In 1884, he was appointed professor of theology at the Free Church College in Glasgow, and began his activity there with his famous lecture "The Contribution of Science to Christianity." A

year earlier, he had published an important book in which
he dealt with the doctrine of evolution: *Natural Law in
the Spiritual World.*

His attempt to look at the universe from a new Christian point of view found a great deal of response in the
entire world, particularly in America, where he was in-
vited in 1893 to deliver the Lowell Lectures. These lectures were published in book form under the title: *The
Ascent of Man* (1894).

What was new in Drummond's approach was that he
did not simply try to attach a theological tail to the Darwinist theory of evolution. Instead, his entire life and
thinking were dominated by a profound religious experience in which he recognized Christ as the central figure
in the history of salvation. It was his innermost urge to
find a meaningful connection between his religious convictions and his scientific knowledge.

As a scientist, he had a general view of the entire history of the forms of life as it was known at the time. It
seemed impossible to him to consider the history of salvation as an isolated and late episode in the total development of man beginning in its archaic initial stages. For
him, the history of salvation could only be meaningful
if it was possible to find its positive connection with the
total development of humanity, in fact with the development of life itself. His paleontological studies and biological research on the origin of species helped him to
overcome the idea of an apparent isolation of the history
of salvation within the total conspectus of divine self-
revelation. He found that, in view of its goal, the total
development of life must instead be seen as part of the
history of salvation.

In order to apply this new viewpoint, it was of primary
importance to start out with a new understanding of Jesus
Christ. In him, the history of salvation widens to become

the history of the total evolution of life. It is aimed at contemporary man but does not find in him its definitive, highest goal, and conclusion. But by the coming of Jesus Christ, man entered into the last phase, that of the approximation to perfection in God.

"Evolution is simply 'history,' a 'history of steps,' a 'general name,' for the history of the steps by which the world has come to be what it is."[31]

"Every step in the proof of the oneness in a universal evolutionary process of this divine humanity of ours is a step in the proof of the divinity of all lower things. And what is of infinitely greater moment, each footprint discovered in the Ascent of Man is a guide to the step to be taken next."[32]

The evolution of man is the "complement and corrective of all other forms of Evolution."[33] Human history is a continuation of evolution on a different level. This does not necessarily mean that evolution in the stage of human history proceeds according to the same laws as in the stage of prehuman life. This is the point where Drummond feels that Darwin and his successors were wrong. History is an area of freedom and consciousness in which evolution has different forms and rules. Evolution finds its conclusion and perfection in the epoch of humanity which was opened by Jesus Christ.

Drummond stated what Teilhard expressed in a similar manner seventy years later—that the aim of evolution for present-day man means " 'to be conformed to the image of his Son' (Rom. 8:29) so that these poor elements may attain to the supreme Beauty."[34]

> The organizing Life being eternal [Drummond says this, not Teilhard] so must Beauty be immortal . . . And more than all there is here fulfilled the sublimest of all prophecies; not Beauty alone but Unity is secured by the Type—Unity of man and man, God

and man, God and Christ and man, till "all shall be one" [Jn. 12:21]. . . .

Hitherto Evolution had no future. It was a pillar with marvellous carving, growing richer and finer towards the top, but without a capital; a pyramid, the vast base buried in the inorganic, towering higher and higher, tier upon tier, life above life, mind above mind, ever more perfect in its workmanship, more noble in its symmetry, and yet withal so much the more mysterious in its aspiration. The most curious eyes, following it upwards, saw nothing . . . The cloud fell and covered it. Just what men wanted to see was hid. The work of the ages had no apex.

But the work begun by Nature is finished by the Supernatural—as we are wont to call the higher natural. And as the veil is lifted by Christianity it strikes men dumb with wonder. For the goal of Evolution is Jesus Christ . . . One Type remains. "Whom he did foreknow, he also did predestinate to be conformed to the image of his Son" [Rom. 8:29]. And "when Christ who is our life shall appear, then shall ye also appear with him in glory" [Col. 3:4].[35]

Drummond drew the same conclusion which we find today in the works of Teilhard de Chardin and which led to such violent attacks against him: The Christian history of salvation is the conclusion and the final summit in the total development of life. In the end, the history of life itself appears to be the history of salvation in its most universal sense in which, and through which, God reveals himself.

Drummond wasn't even afraid to relate the idea of predestination, which underlies the Christian concept of the coming Kingdom of God, to the process of evolution. His book concludes with a universal, visionary tableau in which he connects the Christian expectation of the Kingdom of God with the total development of life: In the field of natural evolution too, "Many are called, but few are chosen" (Mt. 22:14).

A comprehensive view of the whole field of Nature discloses the fact that the circle of the chosen slowly contracts as we rise in the scale of being. Some mineral, but not all, becomes vegetable; some vegetable, but not all, becomes animal; some animal, but not all, becomes human; some human, but not all, becomes Divine. Thus the area narrows. At the base is the mineral, most broad and simple; the spiritual at the apex, smallest, but most highly differentiated. So form rises above form, Kingdom above Kingdom. *Quantity decreases as quality increases.*

The gravitation of the whole system of Nature towards quality is surely a phenomenon of commanding interest. And if among the more recent revelations of Nature there is one thing more significant for Religion than another, it is the majestic spectacle of the rise of Kingdoms towards scarcer yet nobler forms, and simpler yet diviner ends. Of the early stage, the first development of the earth from the nebulous matrix of space, Science speaks with reserve. The second, the evolution of each individual from the simple protoplasmic cell to the formed adult, is proved. The still wider evolution, not of solitary individuals, but of all the individuals within each province—in the vegetal world from the unicellular cryptogam to the highest phanerogam, in the animal world from the amorphous amoeba to Man—is at least suspected, the gradual rise of types being at all events a fact. But now, at last, we see the Kingdoms themselves evolving. And that supreme law which has guided the development from simple to complex in matter, in individual, in sub-Kingdom, and in

Kingdom, until only two or three great Kingdoms remain, now begins at the beginning again, directing the evolution of these million-peopled worlds as if they were simple cells or organisms. Thus, what applies to the individual applies to the family, what applies to the family applies to the Kingdom, what applies to the Kingdom applies to the Kingdoms. And so, out of the infinite complexity there rises an infinite simplicity, the foreshadowing of a final unity, of that

> "One God, one law, one element,
>   And one far-off divine event,
> To which the whole creation moves."
>   (Tennyson, last verses of *In Memoriam*)

This is the final triumph of Continuity, the heart-secret of Creation, the unspoken prophecy of Christianity. To Science, defining it as a working principle, this mighty process of amelioration is simply *Evolution*. To Christianity, discerning the end through the means, it is *Redemption*. These silent and patient processes, elaborating, eliminating, developing all from the first of time, conducting the evolution from millennium to millennium with unaltering purpose and unfaltering power, are the early stages in the redemptive work—the unseen approach of that Kingdom whose strange mark is that it "cometh without observation" [Lk. 17:20]. And these Kingdoms rising tier above tier in ever-increasing sublimity and beauty, their foundations visibly fixed in the past, their progress, and the direction of their progress, being facts in Nature still, are the signs which, since the Magi saw his star in the East, have never been wanting from the firmament of truth, and which in every age, with growing clearness to the wise, and with ever-gathering mystery to the uninitiated, proclaim that "the Kingdom of God is at hand" [Mt. 3:2].[36]

It is impossible in this context, to continue the history of the confrontation of Anglo-Saxon theology with the natural sciences' doctrine of evolution during the last century. What we said about Savage and McCosh gives us only a few glimpses into the recorded discussion, which is much more extensive and far-reaching. Some of it also goes far beyond the problems dealt with by Teilhard de Chardin.

In view of the discussions which were carried on in the United States during the nineteenth century, a modern observer understands quite clearly why some areas of anthropology are missing in the works of Teilhard, particularly an examination of language and its share in evolution. Drummond, on the other hand, deals with language as an accelerating factor in the evolution of man. Because of present efforts toward a new understanding of language, this is of great topical importance. It should be emphasized that Drummond sees a close connection between man's evolution and cerebration, although natural science and medicine were, in his time, quite far from the present level of understanding of the history and structure of the brain. It is also noteworthy that the thinkers mentioned here have given a number of informative views on a possible development of parapsychic capacities as part of the further evolution of man.

A few other American personalities should be mentioned briefly in addition to those Anglo-Saxon theologians with whom we dealt here in more detail.

First of all, there is George Frederick Wright (1838–1921),[37] a famous preacher and, at the same time, one of the best known geologists of the United States. In his youth, he combined his studies with the pursuit of geological interests and carried on research into the geological prehistory of New England. He then specialized in research on the ice age and wrote the standard work *The Ice Age in North America* (1889). At first, he had the chair of New Testament theology at Oberlin College, Ohio. Later, this progressive center of science established a special Chair of the Harmony of Science and Religion for him which he held from 1892 to 1907.

His principal anthropological work in which he laid the foundation for modern paleoanthropology is entitled *Origin and Antiquity of Man* (1912). No less important is his previous book *Scientific Aspects of Christian Evidences*, which was published in New York in 1898. It also deals with Darwinism. Furthermore, Wright is the author of an exceptionally informative autobiography, *Story of My Life and Work*. It offers an insight into the personal and human background of the discussion which took place at that time between theology and natural science.

An equally important contribution to this same discussion was made by Lyman Abbott (1835–1922).[38] Abbott was a lawyer first, then became a Congregational clergyman and a minister at Terre Haute, Indiana. In 1865, he became secretary of the American Union Commission, one of the oldest ecumenical organizations which worked toward co-operation and unification of the numerous Christian denominations in North America. He gained special reputation as an editor of liberal Christian periodicals in which he allowed considerable space to acquaint and confront theology with the results of modern natural science. He was then successively the publisher of such well-known and widely read periodicals as *The Illustrated Christian Weekly* and *Christian Union*. At first, he published *Christian Union* together with Henry Ward Beecher, whom he succeeded at the Plymouth Congregational Church in Brooklyn. The latter had also published a sensational work, *Evolution and Religion* (New York: Fords, 1886).

Later he became publisher of the famous *Outlook*. His principal work, published in 1897, is entitled *Theology of an Evolutionist*. In this book, he gives an extensive review of the results of the work of natural scientists such as Huxley, Tyndall, and Spencer, and proved that the idea of evolution leads to a more profound confirmation of the most important Christian articles of faith. His very informative autobiography, *Reminiscences*, was published in 1905. A later edition of 1923, with an introduction by his son, also gives a report on the last years of his life. Another autobiographical work was published a few years later under the title *What Christianity Means to Me*.

On the occasion of his death, *Outlook* published a special edition on November 8, 1922. It contained a number of contributions by prominent theologians and natural scientists which gave a very vivid picture of his influence upon contemporary theological and scientific circles.

Worthy of special note, in this connection, is the most influential American nature-philosopher of the period, John Fiske of Hartford, Connecticut (1842–1901).[39] A descendant of a Puritan family, he acquired an amazingly universal education at an early age. He was a linguistic genius at the age of twenty and besides being fluent in most modern European languages, also mastered such classical languages as Latin, Greek, Hebrew, Chaldean, Sanskrit, and old Anglo-Saxon.

At Harvard, where he had worked since 1869, he became a follower of Herbert Spencer and worked for sixteen hours every day. During a visit to England, he became personally acquainted with Spencer, Darwin, Huxley, Lewes, Clifford, and Tyndall. In London, he wrote his great work on natural philosophy, *The Outlines of Cosmic Philosophy* (1874). A number of other books followed, in which he dealt with the religious and philosophical consequences of Darwinism, such as *The Unseen World* (1876), *Darwinism and other Essays* (1879), *Excursions of an Evolutionist* (1884), *The Destiny of Man, Viewed in the Light of his Origin* (1884), *The Idea of God, Affected by Modern Knowledge* (1884), *Through Nature to God* (1899), *A Century of Science and Other Essays* (1899). "He was the first to come before the public as a brilliant and courageous defender of the new doctrine of evolution."[40]

The generation which we mention here has, to a large extent, created the conditions for a discussion which could not get off the ground in continental Europe because of the anti-modernist attitude of Catholic theology and a parallel, largely anti-modernist attitude of continental European Protestant circles. It was activated, rather belatedly, by Teilhard de Chardin. It also took a rather long time in the Anglo-Saxon countries for the arguments of the theologians, with whom we dealt above and who tried a Christian interpretation of the doctrine of evolution, to be accepted in the Christian congregations.

A description of the theology of evolution would not be complete without a report on the violent struggle which fundamentalist church circles of all denominations conducted against evolution particularly in the Anglo-Saxon countries. This opposition started in England while Darwin was still alive. It came from the highest church authority. On June 30, 1860, at a memorable session of the British Society in Oxford, Samuel Wilberforce, Anglican Bishop of Oxford, appeared with a host of pugnacious followers of both sexes. With brilliant eloquence and unhampered by any knowledge of the subject matter, he directed a violent attack against Darwin who was not present at this session. The Bishop made extensive use of the method of ridiculing Darwin's theory. For the first time, he cracked the joke which was since repeated innumerable times in anti-Darwinist polemics that, at best, the Darwinists descend from the ape. As a result of this attack against Darwin, which was carried forward with religious wrath, the august assembly forgot about its erstwhile venerable traditions and broke up in an uproar.

The resistance of fundamentalist church circles in the United States was even more lasting. This was particularly the case in the conservative Southern states. Their church affiliation was based on the fundamentalist orientation of the revivalist movement of the nineteenth century.

The dramatic climax of the resistance of conservative church circles against Darwinism was reached in the Scopes trial in Tennessee in 1925.[41] It became worldfamous and is considered one of the most widely known law-cases in modern American ecclesiastical and spiritual history.

On March 25, 1925, the state of Tennessee enacted a law on the basis of which teachers at universities, teachers' colleges, and all other public schools of the state were forbidden to "teach a theory which denies the biblical teaching of the divine creation of man and claims instead that man descended from a lower species of animals."

A small group of liberals decided to establish a test case. They considered this law an unconstitutional interference with freedom of expression and a violation of the constitutional principle of separation of Church and State. It was arranged that, on a certain day, John Thomas Scopes, a twenty-four-year-old teacher of biology, should tell his pupils about Darwin's theory of descent. According to plan, Dr. George Rappleyea of Dayton reported this to the prosecution authorities, and Scopes was arrested on May 7, 1925.

This arrest "developed into one of the most sensational criminal cases of the twentieth century."[42] It was conducted with the most passionate participation of the entire public. Representatives of biblical fundamentalism, such as the public prosecutor and the judge, clashed with the supporters of natural science and liberal theology, such as the defense attorney of the accused, against a background of religious anti-Darwinist demonstrations of all sects.

The jurors brought in a verdict of guilty, and the judge sentenced the accused to pay a fine of $100. An important newspaper guaranteed this amount, whereupon Mr. Scopes was released. He had become world-famous during his incarceration.

Newspapers and periodicals with a pro-Church tendency stated joyfully that the court had made the right choice "between Christ and Darwin." The appellate court quashed the conviction on January 17, 1927, but without declaring the Tennessee anti-evolution law unconstitutional. Later attempts to annul this law—the last one was undertaken in 1951—also remained unsuccessful.

As this famous criminal case shows, it was dangerous in the United States, too, to oppose a theological interpretation of the doctrine of evolution to the biblical fundamentalism of the Church. For them, Darwinism had the sulphur-smell of hell. It is therefore understandable that most of the above-mentioned theologians who tried a positive interpretation of the natural-science doctrine of evolution were "Yankees" from the North. Under the influence of Unitarian theologians, a more liberal climate had developed there.

X

The Beginnings of a Christian Doctrine of Evolution in German Theology and History of Philosophy

It would be rather one-sided to refer solely to the Anglo-Saxon predecessors of Teilhard de Chardin. Actually, Teilhard's ideas are reminiscent of many ideas and terms of seventeenth- and eighteenth-century Christian theosophy and of the Christian religious philosophy of Schelling and Franz von Baader.

The most important elements of Teilhard's ideas are connected with the mainstream of the Swabian spiritual heritage, namely, with Friedrich Christoph Oetinger (1702–82), the father of Swabian Christian theosophy, with his great predecessor, Jacob Boehme (1575–1624) and with his greatest disciple and successor, Friedrich Wilhelm Schelling (1775–1854).[1]

Oetinger was one of the few theologians who tried to re-establish the inner connection between the scientific and the Christian outlook on the universe. In his *Theologia ex idea vitae deducta* (1765), he draws a picture of the history of salvation as a history of the total development of life through all its stages. Oetinger was the first theologian who wanted to include in his theological understanding the larger world that had been discovered in his time by natural science, geologists, physicists, physicians, and psychologists.

His point of departure was the idea of God as the *ens manifestativum sui*. God is not the finite, definable God of the theologians who put a ready-made man into a pre-fabricated world. He is rather that force which strives from a dark original cause toward revelation, that is, toward his own realization and corporealization. He manifests himself gradually in the development of life in its various stages. Physics belong to his revelation just as much as the history of salvation in the proper sense.[2] The entire universe is included in the process of transformation and transfiguration which will reach its conclusion in a history of salvation hastening toward the second coming of Jesus. The *physica sacra* is a prerequisite of the history of salvation.[3] "Corporeality," that is, the corporeal manifestation and unfolding of the inner plenitude of divine existence, the self-expression in a universe which is transfigured to become the Kingdom of God—this corporeality "is the end of the paths of God."[4]

Oetinger has grasped and understood the cosmic aspect of redemption to the fullest extent. Teilhard sees the problem from the same angle because of his knowledge of modern physics, geology, and paleontology. But he ignored the clarifying term "corporeality." Instead, he refers to "sacred matter."

Oetinger also believes that the development of life aims toward the human manifestation of God in Jesus Christ. He understands Christ as the historical point of departure for a cosmic process of transformation of the world. Through this process, divine life enters the stream of temporal life and the transformation of humanity begins as it becomes part of the growing body of Christ. For both Teilhard and Oetinger the incarnation is not a historical fact which happened once. It is rather the inauguration of a new way of life for humanity, the beginning of a new form of existence for the spirit, materialized into a body, which first becomes manifest in Jesus Christ. But each redeemed man will be included. Going beyond man, this spirit embraces, penetrates and thoroughly leavens the entire earth. Corporeality is the end of all roads of God. What Teilhard calls *christification* is not expressed in the same terms by Oetinger, but, in effect, he expresses the same thought by calling it the conclusion, goal, and terminal point of the future development of humanity and, through humanity, of the entire universe. The conclusion of the transformation of the universe is its transformation into human shape, namely, that of Christ.

The decisive influence for Oetinger was that of his great teacher Jacob Boehme, from whom he received the real inspiration for his *Theologia ex idea vitae deducta.* Jacob Boehme knew nothing about paleoanthropology, nor did he collect jawbones of fossil hominids. But he expressed the basic idea of Christian anthropology more clearly than Teilhard, the idea of "man being struck by the image of Christ."[5] When Adam turned away from God, he was "struck" by the image of Christ in the very moment of his estrangement. Christ was shown to him as the future image of his revival, integration, and exaltation, as the goal of his future. Adam was never left to himself. The image of Christ was given to him as a model which accompanied him through all phases of the development of human consciousness, as the aim into which he should be molded and transformed.

This aim was at first a promise. But then, after its fulfillment through Jesus Christ, it became a force of transformation, an "inauguration" of a new form of existence, an element of the progressive incorporation of pious humanity into the body of Christ, the beginning of a progressive permeation of humanity with resurrection as the new form of existence, a transformation of humanity, and thereby of the universe, into the corporeal form of the Spirit.

This line is then continued by Schelling. In his philosophy of nature, he is very strongly influenced by Oetinger. In his *Philosophie der Mythologie* and also in his

later work *Die Weltalter,* we find a further speculative
development of Oetinger's basic thought of God as the
ens manifestativum sui and of incarnation as the great
turning point of the development of humanity toward a
new manifestation of the corporeal form of the Spirit.

Schelling also wants to find the divine purpose of the
earth. He sees the future as a scientific enlightenment of
the progressive self-revelation of God in the physical and
spiritual world. In *Die Weltalter* he says (1811): "It appears that it was the privilege of our age to open forever
the road to the objectivity of science." The objectivity of
science means to him a combination of scientific knowledge of the physical world with that of the spiritual
world, toward which he has striven himself. Thus he continues:

> As long as it (that is, science) is restricted to the
> internal, it lacks the natural means of external pres-
> entation. Now, after a long time of confusion, we re-
> member nature again and science has remembered
> the former unity with nature. But it did not stop at
> this point. No sooner were the first steps toward re-
> unification with nature taken than it had to be recog-
> nized how very old the physical was. Far from being
> the last, it is rather the first, with which everything
> begins, including the development of divine life.
> Since then, science does not draw any more from
> faraway ideas to descend from them to the natural.
> On the contrary, it starts from the unconscious exist-
> ence of the eternal and leads it upwards toward su-
> preme transfiguration in divine consciousness. Trans-
> cendental thoughts now receive physical strength
> and life. Conversely, nature becomes more and more
> the visible reproduction of the loftiest terms.[6]

Schelling then begins to prophesy: "Only ignorant people are looking with contempt upon the physical. But, in

a short time, this, too, will end and the sentence will again become true that 'the stone which the builders rejected has become the chief cornerstone.' "[7]

Schelling has thus indicated the inner line of intellectual and scientific development of humanity which leads straight to Teilhard de Chardin in our time. In the century since Schelling's death, the idea of evolution in its manifold interpretations has eventually prevailed after it was repeatedly examined, confirmed, and rejected. It is impossible for a Christian understanding of the world, of the history of mankind and of the universe to ignore this knowledge. In the long run, a presentation of the truth of the Christian faith cannot be based on a form of interpretation that has lost its live connection with present knowledge about the world. Otherwise, there is a danger that the dogma will become a museum for the history of dogma in a world which thinks along completely different lines. Schelling had a presentiment of this new task.

Meanwhile, a new and tremendous forward thrust was made to enlighten the world through natural science. The inner structures and movements of the atom were explored. The findings about the construction of the atom were used to manipulate atomic energy. This is where Teilhard de Chardin inserts a new lever. He follows the tracks of former efforts to clear up the divine secret and the promises of this world and to fathom the course of revelation of God from its beginnings to its consummation.

These ideas of late-pietist theosophy and of the religious philosophy of romanticism and idealism penetrated rather sparingly into the official Protestant theology of the nineteenth century. However, we find some thinkers among the university theologians of the twentieth century who have tried to apply systematic thought, from a Christian point of view, to the idea of evolution proscribed by the Church.

In this connection, we have to refer particularly to Karl Beth's book *Der Entwicklungsgedanke und das Christentum*. It was published in Berlin in 1909, and deals systematically with the question whether and to what extent the idea of evolution could be applied to a Christian understanding of the histories of creation and salvation. Beth held the chair of systematic theology. He opposed the rejection of the theory of evolution, a popular attitude in wide church circles, and showed a number of points of contact between evolutionist thinking and Christian understanding of the world.

> All development is creation. The first creation must be seen and understood in such a way that future development is already inherent within it. Development is the method of divine creation, since it must be assumed that the first creation of the world was accomplished with all future development in mind. In the terminology of the religious concept, man is therefore the result of immediate divine creation, not only in regard to his mind but, to no lesser extent, in regard to his body. This is true although the various stages of development which are the origin of man's body, are much more clearly visible than those which are the origin of his mind.[8]

Karl Beth assures us very emphatically that the interpretation of the Christian idea of creation in light of the doctrine of evolution is the only appropriate one and the only one which can be called responsible from a theological point of view. In this connection, he refers with special emphasis to Paul. In his letter to the Romans, Paul states that there is a direct connection between the salvation of man and the salvation of the universe: "For the creation waits with eager longing for the revealing of the sons of God; for the creation was subjected to futility, not of its own will but by the will of him who subjected it in hope, because the creation itself will be set free from its bondage to decay and obtain the glorious liberty of the children of God. We know that until now the whole creation has been groaning in travail together" (8:19–22). Beth comments on this passage as follows:

> The entire tremendous process of coming into existence and of development of the world of nature up to the creation of humanity can thus be conceived as the method by which a creature endowed with reason and believing in ethical principles is formed. From that point onwards, it climbs, within itself, to a new and peculiar stage of development of its spiritual existence . . . The main thought is that the essence of nature is birth. It endeavors to produce something new, something higher out of itself and thus to transform its own existence to higher clarity. The total creature goes through this self-development in a fearful struggle in expectation of a future state of "freedom in glory." This will be reached, once humanity has finally grasped its religio-ethical goal. This main thought is not a remote one for us. It means that once those creatures which are endowed with reason and ethical principles will have reached the highest stage of development, the development of those which are not endowed with reason will be concluded as well. This large part of creation has been in a state of constant development toward a higher formation and has been helpful in working out the upper limits for the education of mankind.[9] . . . Thus it is the idea of evolution, as formulated in the doctrine of descent, which preserves the Christian idea of God from disparagement.[10]

It is the place of man in the general order of descent which allows us to recognize his central position within the development of life. "As we emphasize that it is possible to include man in the general process of development as its last stage, we show that he is the climax which God wanted to give to creation. He was formed by an immeasurably long process. Now, at the end of the process, he is trying to recall its course and meaning. He recognizes that he was himself the goal of creation."

Among the manifold conclusions which Beth draws from the application of the doctrines of evolution and descent upon a modern understanding of the Christian doctrines of creation and the end of time, there is one which deserves special attention. It is the attempt to outline a new understanding of the connection between the Christian history of salvation and the history of religion: "Religion has a history. It is a history of development. Divine revelation itself is history. It is its evolutionary factor."

Christian history of salvation cannot be separated from the general history of religion. It is part of the development of the universal revelation of God which takes place in the total history of religion. "While religion is not formed according to the program of descent, it has an evolutionary history. It is based upon the universally prevailing divine revelation. Depending upon circumstances and upon conditions which will be brought about by the freedom of the ultimate spirits, God will 'draw' (Jn. 6:44) men from all over the world to himself."[11]

Accordingly, Beth does not consider the significance of Jesus as a unique irruption of an event of salvation into human history. He rather believes that it is the beginning of a new stage of development. Its aim is the progressive transformation of humanity into a form of existence initiated by Jesus Christ. "Man's stage of organization on earth is of an interim character and will be followed by a higher stage which was opened, in principle, for all men by the Jesus-revelation."[12]

Beth finishes his book with a statement which leads directly to the ideas of Teilhard de Chardin:

> Christian faith itself, which strives for live perception, has a special concern. It wants to see the world, humanity, the work of God, and human life from the angle of evolution. Through the idea of evolution both religious faith and the understanding of the world find the key for the riddle of existence and development in a sentence of the founder of embryology, K. E. von Baer: "The history of nature is nothing but the history of progressive victories of mind over matter." After all this, we can replace the often-encountered enmity between Christianity and the idea of evolution by a certain elective affinity between the two ideas.[13]

However, at the time of its publication, Beth's book did not receive the attention which it deserved on account of its subject matter. Beth himself was unaware of the attempts in the Anglo-Saxon world of the nineteenth century to find a Christian interpretation of the doctrine of evolution. For the reasons we have already mentioned, contemporary theologians were not familiar with this kind of topic. They were primarily interested in questions of historical criticism related to the Old and New Testaments, patristic church traditions, and in topics of the incipient Luther renaissance. Beth's works thus never aroused the attention of the theologians and natural scientists of his time, which is surprising considering how topical the problem he posed himself is nowadays.

Besides Karl Beth, the systematic scholar, a number of other personalities who belonged to the great outsiders of their generation in the fields of natural science and religious philosophy have to be mentioned. They have consciously carried on and continued the tradition of Boehme, Oetinger, Schelling, and Von Baader. Considering the present situation and problems of theology and anthropology, the outsider position of these thinkers proves to be the position of isolation common to all prophets.

Teilhard de Chardin combined outstanding knowledge of paleontology and paleoanthropology with the search for a new Christian view of the universe and the history of salvation in which the findings of natural science and theology would form a unity. If Teilhard is considered unique for this reason, then it is only just and fair to point out that a similar attempt was previously undertaken by one of his German contemporaries and professional colleagues, whose works he did not know either, although they were mostly published in the period between the First and Second World Wars.

We refer to Edgar Dacqué, the director of the Munich museum of paleontology, which was destroyed in an air attack. He was a profoundly religious Protestant Christian. He was deeply concerned to find a meaningful connection between his paleontological and paleoanthropological findings and his Christian understanding of creation, history of salvation, and the end of time.

In his book *Der Deszendenzgedanke und seine Geschichte vom Altertum bis zur Neuzeit* (Munich, 1903), we find numerous indications of basic points for a Christian interpretation and further evolution.

Like Teilhard de Chardin and, before him, Schelling and Oken, Dacqué considers nature as the place for the manifestation of man. In fact, it is itself equal to developed man. Dacqué draws a parallel to his interpretation with "the seemingly contrary theory of descent in natural science . . . purporting that, in the course of the history of the earth, man has traversed all stages, from the one-cell water-animal . . . up to quaternary man."[14] Man is "a creature of its own kind, a breed of its own, from the very beginning. It was man who released representatives of the animal world from his breed, and not vice versa."[15]

More than in previous works, the influence of Jacob Boehme, the theologian of nature, comes to the fore in his book *Die Urgestalt* (1940, 2d ed. 1944). The speculative thoughts of a Christian theosophy come out even more clearly in it, and he expresses these thoughts more precisely:

His (that is, man's) original form was therefore already metaphysically present in the organic kingdom. This means that it was "willed" by God in earliest times, when the first and lowest kinds of creatures were brought forth. Although, chronologically speaking, man, as fully developed man, appeared only in the last period of the earth, he was already present in all living creatures, uncounted millions of years ago . . . The organic world which is represented in spread-out form in the history of the earth, has many types which developed and disappeared. Successively, they advance from the lower to the higher type of organization. This means that, chronologically, man is the last one. Only thus, the tree of life which goes through all ages of prehistory is actually the "genealogical tree of man." If we want to maintain the basic idea of natural development—and as natural scientists we pretty well have to do that—we arrive at the inescapable conclusion that man is the "original form" on which everything alive is based. And, to repeat it again, this has to be understood as follows: No known species or form of our world or of prehistory is shaped in such a way that it could be included in the genealogical tree of man as the highest type of creature. They all developed outside of the path which leads to that height. However, if all this is an outside development, and if, as we believe, there is a connection in natural history and in development be-

tween all creatures and man, then man, as the final
climax, must also be the common "original form" of
the organic kingdom.[16]

What is particularly significant in the work of Dacqué
is his attempt to use the tradition of myths to interpret
previous forms of human consciousness and previous
stages of development. Dacqué believes that myths are
remnants of ancient recollections of prehistoric forms of
existence and stages of consciousness of man. Obviously,
it was just this interpretation of myths which was particularly conducive toward shocking contemporary scholars in the field of anthropology and paleoanthropology
whose orientation was entirely positivistic. It also led to
most violent opposition.

Dacqué's ideal was the combination of science and
myth which, according to him, "have to be combined to
form reality."[17] It is significant for the rationalist attitude
of Teilhard that he never became involved in this problem. It has an old tradition in German mystical theology
from Albertus Magnus via Jacob Boehme, up to Schelling's
philosophy of the myth, and the natural philosophy of
German idealism and German romanticism.

According to Dacqué, myths and legends report of "pre-
cenozoic" events. "Primeval, real life talks to us here from
far away, through the confused and recast legends. It
shows us man of the mesozoic age of the earth in this
highly demoniacal milieu, fleeing in fright or fighting,
and often victorious or defeated. Why doubt something
which prehistoric man has seen alive? It was handed
down in legends because those were overpowering impressions of nature upon the childlike, receptive emotions of our forefathers and these impressions were often
decisive in the life of peoples."[18]

It is particularly the individual interpretation of myths
which aroused the opposition of his professional col-

leagues. An example is the legends of the one-eyed man, that is, the cyclops Polyphemus or Utnapishtim in the Gilgamesh Epic. Here the legends preserved a recollection of what the "amphibian or earthbound original type of human life" saw two hundred million years ago, and at the latest in the final stage of the paleozoic period, namely, that members or relatives of the human species had the unpaired parietal eye (parietal organ). For, at that time, crabs and vertebrate animals still had "fully developed" parietal organs, which were later mostly "reverted" (for example, to become a pineal gland). Also the "fish-man legends . . . draw such a distinct picture that it could be possible in life." They reflect recollections of early human types in fish shape. The legend of horny Siegfried also transmits the memory of the stegocephalians of the Paleozoic and their skin skeleton.[19]

By the mythical interpretation of individual results of paleontological research, Dacqué had aroused the opposition of his colleagues, the natural scientists. But the theologians opposed him, too, because he considered the traditions of the Old and New Testaments as part of the mythical traditions of humanity. What they did not realize was that Dacqué believed in an inner connection between myth and revelation as given by Schelling in his *Philosophie des Mythos* and *Philosophie der Offenbarung*.

For Dacqué, the present shape of man is not the end of human development, either. For him, too, the turn to the "New Man," the breakthrough to a new phase of human development, begins with incarnation. For him, too, the appearance of the historical figure of Jesus Christ is not an event of past history which only happened once, but the beginning of a process of "christianization" of the world.

"There is a primeval wisdom that the organic kingdom is man, taken apart. But the proposition that man is a microcosm and that the great universe is his image—or vice versa—gets, as we see, its true meaning only if we look at the original shape of man." But "in us, too, the original shape of man is veiled, solidified, willfully extroverted, mortally broken in time and afflicted with death . . . Thus our full human status as such cannot be part of the tree of all life. It is rather an organic feature of an ideal tree of life, while being itself finite and mortal. As all animal forms at the end of time, physical man forms a special branch of the total genealogical tree, only as a symbol, which really 'means' Eternal Man.

"Thus earthly man, sublime as his natural form may be, joins the rest of nature 'in expectation' of perfect man who, in a new way, shall be the true image and facsimile of God. Present earthly man will become 'extinct' and will be replaced by a new, more perfect man. In his innermost being, he really 'aims' toward this new form of man, he carries it within himself, he wants to give expression to it, as subhuman nature once aimed for and was pregnant with him."[20]

As in the case of Teilhard de Chardin, Dacqué's anthropology leads to Christology:

Christ has brought the certainty that out of our inner human self will come progress toward healing and redemption. By his preaching, by his death, and then by his resurrection, he has revealed to us the true new spirituality, in which God himself is present. Only now do we begin to understand how much his death is filled with superhuman meaning of the hereafter.

Does this mean that he will lead us and nature back to Paradise? Certainly not. For the Paradise of the demiurge has been overcome in God himself. The re-creation of man in the original birth of the new form of divine man will be a human prototype

of a quite different order, of different content and
character than the original form of what was once
the man of Paradise . . . In the broken world, after
the end of Paradise, all those beings, begotten by
the ever-present force of the Word of God, will, in
their own way, recover to partake of the new transfiguration. With the human soul and its salvation,
each and every soul in nature will be "christianized."
They will live in a hierarchically organized kingdom,
in which everyone will have his proper place and his
proper space to live in, as a fulfilled "body of God."[21]

The vision of the "christianization" of humanity already anticipates the idea and the terminology of Teilhard de Chardin's "christification" (see pages 219–20).

Dacqué was a thinker for whose ideas and insights his
time was not yet ripe. His attempt to give a simultaneous
view of the insights derived from natural science and the
basic ideas of a Christian understanding of man and the
universe can only be appreciated today as a result of the
new discussion set into motion by Teilhard de Chardin.

A confrontation with the evolutionist thinking of modern natural science also occurred in the case of another
great outsider of German philosophy of religion and culture. Contrary to the present wave or fashion of existentialism which holds the philosophy of German universities in its grip, Leopold Ziegler has endeavored, by lonely
thought and meditation, to continue the great traditions
of German idealistic philosophy, particularly that of
Schelling, in an independent, speculative way. In the
solitude of his "Efeu-Häusle" in Überlingen on Lake
Constance, he wrote his book *Die Überlieferung*. In it, he
has not only given a new view of the inner connection
and continuity of the great spiritual traditions of European intellectual history; he has also, as Schelling before

him, endeavored to get a new synopsis of a philosophical understanding of nature and history.

From the beginning, Leopold Ziegler's philosophical reflection gravitates around the problem of "Universal Man" as we find it in the philosophy of Franz von Baader. These efforts not only help him to throw light upon the road of philosophical anthropology in pre-Christian philosophy and its fulfillment in the figure of Jesus Christ; his anthropological thinking also leads him back to early history and prehistory, and he tries to find the proper place for the human phenomenon in the total development of life. His ideas on these connections are already indicated in his booklet *Über die Welt des Organismus* (Munich, 1949), in which he gives a critique of the application of mechanical thinking upon the contemplation of nature and history. He writes there as follows:

> He who thinks *mechanistically* is bound to say that everything which exists has existed before in countless cyclical repetitions and will come to existence again. But he who thinks *organically* breathes with relief that there is no such methodical desolation of the world. Indeed, during every day of pulsating life he does not know what may yet happen in this world. There was a development from the trilobites of the Cambrian to the saurians of the Jurassic period, from the foraminifera in the chalk formation to the diluvian primates and it may be followed by a development from present-day man to the superman of the next great metamorphosis of this or another, nobler planet.[22]

Without knowing Teilhard de Chardin, Leopold Ziegler gives us a general sketch of the goal toward which the evolution of life is aiming. It will lead to the jump of evolution from the present man to the superman. Like Teilhard de Chardin, he believes that the moving force is not the evolutionary push from behind, but the forward pull which considers each higher stage of evolution as the fulfillment of an image of promise which flashes up in the previous stage as a model of future development.

"Therefore the last, just-noticeable tendency of life is the mystical urge to transcend reality in its present form again and again. In view of the possibilities to make the organic visible, all that exists has only temporary meaning. Life will always be geared either to surpass itself or to disavow itself as something provisional. Our intelligence, however, which merely imitates the creations of nature, is inclined to think that nature must have, in its imagination, something like a model of what it is going to create in the future."[23]

In the final analysis, Ziegler's idea of evolution is determined by the Christian pattern of promise and fulfillment.

The widening of the concept of history, which is so significant for evolutionary thinking, can also be found in Ziegler's works. We already saw it when dealing with Savage and Drummond. Thus he can say: "A body like this planet earth is generally considered to be inorganic. If we were to succeed in understanding it in organic terms and prove a series of changes in its form, over a period of time, then the knowledge about these changes would undoubtedly be real history."[24]

Like Teilhard de Chardin, he sees the total evolution of life as a kind of spiral which is winding toward the top. Its inner axis is Universal Man who evolves toward the model of Christ: "Maybe the time will come when, through widely or narrowly wound spirals, we shall reach ever higher levels on which we shall perceive the one and unique figure of all figures. This will be the splendid opening of a prospect for a special immortality of character and physiognomy. Thus our own miserable time in which the world is led forward impetuously but aimlessly may yet get a cruelly reduced share of that austere period which nature had urged us so frequently and benevolently to revere."[25]

Eight years later, in 1956, the *Lehrgespräch vom allgemeinen Menschen* brings the great and mature synopsis of his anthropology. In this last of the great works of his old age, Ziegler returns to the concept of Universal Man which was the key term of his total philosophical development. It also dominates his book *Die Menschwerdung*, and his work entitled *Die Überlieferung* for a reason which is connected with the innermost purpose of this work: His elucidation of the "tradition" of Western spiritual history and rediscovery of its prophetic root has made him recognize that the center of human history is the genesis of Universal (that is, Eternal) Man in the figure of Jesus Christ. The inner connection "between the Word, who is with God, the first Adam, who was created in God's image, and the second Adam, Christ, the New Man," struck him with the clarity of a divine manifestation.[26]

But his universal spirit urged him on to recognize the secret of man in a deeper context. It is true that history and authenticity are the true spheres of man. But this history takes place on the nature-bound level of many other stages of the development of life, which are interrelated in continuous evolution. What is man's attitude toward the development of life in the areas of life which preceded him? What especially is his attitude toward the animal kingdom, from which he undoubtedly descended? Scientific anthropology has made a number of irrefutable findings establishing the connections between man and the *regnum animale*. Compared to them, all reflections on Eternal Man and Universal Man may appear like arbitrary mythology and could, at best, be excused as pious poetry or "ideologies." Could a biologist and a scientific anthropologist not make light of all this?

Already in the reflections of the *Menschwerdung* the question is asked casually whether the image of Eternal Man or Universal Man did not actually exist at the beginning of anthropogenesis and whether it did not from the very beginning determine the evolution of life through its various areas. The *Lehrgespräch* represents the attempt to establish the connection between the image of Universal Man in present-day findings of natural science on the position of man in the total course of evolution and his descent from the animal kingdom. Behind Ziegler's effort there is not only an unflagging research into modern biological and scientific-anthropological literature, but also a multitude of most intensive discussions with friends who were zoologists and biologists.

In these "dialogues" it is established, step by step, by way of a Socratic dialogue between philosopher and biologist that, in the final analysis, Universal Man is the leading concept for the development of life itself.

In his philosophy of art, Ziegler's *Apollons letzte Epiphanie* turns away from the older theory of descent of natural science. Art is not the genesis of the higher out of the lower, but the revelation of Universal Man from above. In like manner, there is a no less Copernican change of viewpoint in his concept that we can understand the evolution of life only if the traditional theory of descent be reversed: Something "higher" cannot evolve out of something "lower." Man can never "emerge" out of a series of animals, unless the "higher" was, from the very outset, the leading concept, the inner model. As the "final goal" it prodded evolution onward from the inside toward its final destination, which means toward its complete realization, manifestation, and corporeality.

And finally, what is Universal Man, who is Universal Man? Who is he, or what is he, who, as far as we were able to elucidate, descended from Universal

Animal? He originated with time and in time, he was driven onward, unconsciously but unerringly toward a certain goal, namely, liberation from the environment in which he was imprisoned. But, even now, while still not a freed man of nature in *statu perficiendi*, he is already, in *statu nascendi*, one to be liberated in the future. Thus he is not freeborn, but dedicated to freedom and penetrating to it. As such, he begins to escape from his environment and the contemporary world with a child's pattering steps, as it were. With innumerable antennae he begins to adjust himself to the world, searching for it, and being searched for by it. Although the interpretation may be different, we hardly overreach ourselves if we apply to Universal Man the sentence of Baalschem: "Over the suns and over the earths Messiah wanders in a thousand shapes. And the suns and the earths are maturing to meet him."[27]

Man is unfinished, but on the road to perfection. He has not been freed by nature yet; he is still imprisoned, but he will be liberated in the future because he is on the road to liberation. Present man is the embryo of future man, still involved in his individuality, but on the road to transformation into Universal, Eternal, Divine Man. As the prototype for the final plan, man represents the inner model for the unfolding of life. Within his religious consciousness, the various phases of development are dominated by one final goal, namely, the "Word incarnate." The various forms which man assumed during the millennia of his history are the thousand shapes of the one Messiah who wanders over the earth. This is the essence of Ziegler's philosophy.

This concept in Leopold Ziegler's "dialogue" has special significance because he develops it by an original continuation of the ideas of Hegel and Schelling. The existentialists currently make light of the great thinkers of the speculative philosophy of German idealism. Contrary to them, Ziegler discovers the powerful meaning for the future to be derived particularly from Hegel's *Phenomenology of Mind*. In his private conversations, he also points out repeatedly that the exhaustive interpretation of this book would be one of the great tasks of the future of humanity and of the determination of human nature and history. He also considered Schelling's *Weltalter* as a prophetic work, the meaning of which could only be fathomed by a future humanity.[28]

What Ziegler has in mind, in this connection, is, basically, the reduction of Hegel's dialectics of history to their original theological foundations. The end of the movement of history occurs in the epiphany of the Son of Man, of "Perfect Man," in whom the movement and development of existence is completed. The evolution of life is a tremendous process which passes through both nature and history. Cosmogony and anthropogeny appear as the one widely stretched and tension-filled road to the self-realization, self-revelation, and self-corporealization of God, the *ens manifestativum sui*.

In conclusion, we can therefore say that Universal Man is the divine original image and prototype, the basis for the development of all forms of the *regnum animale* in its immeasurable variety. It is then realized on a higher level in humanity, whose universal history is, in the last analysis, identical with the history of salvation.

Thus we saw Universal Man ascend from Universal Animal, or more precisely, within Universal Animal, of which, in a deeper sense, he was and is an "earlier stage." Universal Man is working irresistibly, all the time, as the cycle of all cycles of theogony, cosmogony, and anthropogeny and therefore as one single, continuous, forward, and backward manifestation of

God, the universe, and man. By whatever name we call him, that carrier and mediator with the never-failing memory, whether we call him the restorer or the one who will arrive, standing up and floating in the air, he will always merge into the image of the Son of Man of revelation . . . I am the first and the last. I am the immemorial, the uninjured, and the injured. My body is in all that is corporeal; I am nailed on the cross with all flesh; my body is devoid of all corporeality. I am death and resurrection; I am transformation and life. I am the reversion, the return, and the homecoming. I am the reappearance and the restoration.[29]

XI

Sri Aurobindo's Doctrine of Evolution and the Future of Man

When dealing with the Christian understanding of creation and the end of time, it may appear like an irrelevant digression to turn our attention to a religious philosopher of Hinduism who, as a Hindu, took a very critical attitude to Christianity. But our topic makes it advisable to have a look at Sri Aurobindo. This most universal mind among the leaders of modern Hinduism has attempted to reach a new understanding of the future of man and humanity by a bold reinterpretation of the theory of evolution. His image shows amazing agreement with similar European conceptions. This shows the universal character of the transformation of religious anthropology which takes place under the influence of the doctrine of evolution.

The distinctive feature of Aurobindo's approach is that he has not only given a new theoretical image of the future of man, but that he claims to be a representative realization of this image himself. He has created an important pedagogical institution, the Aurobindo Ashram,[1] in which integral Yoga, developed by him, is being practiced in order to get man ready for the irruption of the superhuman and the supramental. It is a pedagogical experiment on the largest scale by which Aurobindo is distinguished quite clearly from analogous, purely ideological projects in the West.

What distinguishes Aurobindo from other leaders of modern Hinduism, such as Ramakrishna and Gandhi, is that he has absorbed European education and intellectual traditions since his youth in Europe. As a result, his attitude to Western thinking was less prejudiced and his knowledge of it far superior to that of other Indian thinkers. They could never free themselves entirely from the convulsive pathos of the constantly emphasized contrast between the alleged spirituality of India and the alleged materialism of the West.

But Aurobindo's father, a physician, felt differently about it. He was convinced of the superiority of Western over Indian culture and sent his son to England at the age of seven. He wanted him to grow up in Western culture and Western thought and not to have any contact with the Indian spiritual heritage.

At King's College, Cambridge, Aurobindo distinguished himself by his brilliant gifts and an unusual knowledge superior to that of all English students. He passed the entrance examination for Indian public service with distinction, but managed to prevent his acceptance into Indian public service as an official of the British colonial administration. Although this was the dream of every Indian studying in England, Aurobindo managed to get himself disqualified in horseback-riding, an important requirement.

This development was quite handy for the British authorities. Contrary to the educational plans of his father, Aurobindo had become a fervent Indian nationalist in Cambridge. For a long time he had been on the black list as a member of a revolutionary group of Indian students who had chosen the romantic name of "Lotus and Dagger." Its members had sworn a solemn oath that they would dedicate all their knowledge and wealth to the liberation of India from British colonial rule.

Aurobindo, who had been sent out at the age of seven to become a good Englishman, thus returned to India in 1893 as a fanatical Indian nationalist and revolutionary. The already existing Indian Congress planned to gain inpendence by legal means. Aurobindo tried, from the very first day, to convert it into an instrument of revolutionary action.

He was involved in a bomb plot in Muzaffarpur directed against the British District Judge Kingsford. Instead of the judge, an English couple, completely unconnected with the matter, were killed. About one hundred extremists were arrested, among them Aurobindo. During the trial, which went into the history of the Indian liberation movement as the famous Alipur Case, he was the main defendant and was detained in the prison of Calcutta. There he underwent the profound transformation from revolutionary politician to prophet of integral Yoga. He had been influenced by a number of divine visions which moved him deeply and pulled him away from the path of life and direction of thought which he had previously followed.

These visionary experiences opened within him a new center of perception and inspired him to new creative activity. He left the territory which was under the sovereignty of the British Crown and went to the small French colony of Pondicherry. He resisted all temptations of his former friends and comrades in arms who wanted him to return to politics, and founded the Ashram which comprises today about one quarter of the city of Pondicherry. It consists of an entire system of schools, from kindergarten to university, modern recreation-grounds, a stadium, hundreds of modern residential buildings, numerous installations for artisans, workshops, a power station, a print shop, a publishing house and ultra-modern agricultural installations.

In Pondicherry, Aurobindo proclaimed and realized the new man, the *superman*. The point of departure for Aurobindo's image of man is also the idea that man is a creature which, by its nature, pushes beyond itself and ever tries to widen the limits of its consciousness. The chaotic symptoms of crisis in our time are connected with deep-reaching developments in the intellectual, political, and economic area. They make integration imperative. These symptoms are proof to him that a new stage of human evolution is imminent. Later on, Teilhard de Chardin was to argue in a similar way.

This next stage of man's evolution will be brought about by the irruption of the supramental. Human nature has an irrepressible urge for higher perceptions, for a more intimate way of communication with the divine, for a more intensive form of communion among men. The most visible expression of this urge to reach beyond one-self is the longing for the miracle. "The supernatural is the nature which we have not attained or do not yet know, or the means of which we have not yet conquered. The common taste for miracles is the sign that man's ascent is not yet finished."[2]

The divine perfection of human existence is the aim of this ascent. "Evolution is not yet finished, reason is not the last word nor the reasoning animal the supreme figure of nature. As man emerged out of the animal, so out of man the superman emerges."[3] "Animal man is the ob-scure starting-point, the present natural man, varied and tangled, the mid-road, but supernatural man is the luminous and transcendent goal of our human journey."[4] "If men only caught a glimpse of what infinite enjoyments, what perfect forces, what luminous reaches of spontaneous knowledge, what wide calms of our being lie waiting for us in the tracts which our animal evolution has not yet conquered, they would leave all and never rest till they had gained these treasures."[5]

Aurobindo has absorbed and assimilated the spiritual tradition of Hinduism in an amazingly profound way. But what he aims for is quite different from the traditional guiding images of Hinduism. In the spiritual field, too, he is a personality of distinctly revolutionary character for

India, principally because of his approximation to certain basic concepts of the Christian idea on the course and goal of the history of salvation.

Aurobindo is the first spiritual leader of the Hindu tradition to have broken with the radical dualism of Indian thinking. Not flight from the world but affirmation of the world appears to be the decisive task for him. He says:

> If the world is ruled by the flesh and the devil, all the more reason that the children of Immortality should be here to conquer it for God and the Spirit . . . We regard the world not as an invention of the devil or a self-delusion of the soul, but as a manifestation of the Divine, even though as yet this manifestation is still partial, still progressing in its evolution. Therefore, for us renunciation of life cannot be the goal of life nor rejection of the world the object for which the world was created. We seek to realize our unity with God, but for us that realization involves a complete and absolute recognition of our unity with man and we cannot cut the two asunder. To use Christian language, the Son of God is also the Son of Man and both elements are necessary to the complete Christhood.[6]

Another new facet introduced by him is the affirmation of personality, of personal and individual values. No abolition of the ego, no destruction of personality, no dissolution in Nirvana, but the attainment of true personality is his goal. Meeting the personal God—this is also a new departure in Indian spiritual history—destroys man's "egohood" but establishes him as a person. By this meeting, it becomes true personality. "Therefore, when the heart and life turn toward the highest and the infinite, they arrive not at an abstract existence, a Sat or else a Nirvana, but at an existent; not merely at a consciousness, but at a conscious Being; not merely at a purely impersonal delight of the Is, but at a finite I am of bliss."[7]

The third decisively new motif of Aurobindo is evolution, an idea with which he became acquainted when dealing with Western philosophy and natural science. "A form of life must be born which is closer to God. If this is not the way, then there is no other way for the human species."[8]

The extent to which the idea of evolution dominates Aurobindo's thinking is confirmed by the fact that the French disciple of Aurobindo and present director of the International University of the Aurobindo Ashram, P. B. Saint-Hilaire, wrote an introduction to an Aurobindo-anthology under the title: *The Future Evolution of Man.* It consists of excerpts from the works of Aurobindo, namely, *The Life Divine, The Human Cycle,* and *The Synthesis of Yoga,* which are presented in systematic order and with short explanations and notes.[9]

According to the opinion of Saint-Hilaire, the criterion of evolution was apparently best suited to give an account of the total structure of Aurobindo's system of thought on the position of man and his future form. This approach is quite pertinent, because the entire complex of the idea of evolution represented that portion of Aurobindo's thinking in which, in his personal development, the fusion took place between the scientific and philosophical traditions of the West and the spiritualistic traditions of Indian, particularly Vedic philosophy. His religious self-understanding also used to express itself most appropriately in these terms. On the other hand, this complex of the idea of evolution also represents the area in which Western disciples and readers of Aurobindo can most easily understand the principal purpose of his "Integral Yoga."

However, the development of the new and higher form of life is not the result of one's own effort, in the manner

of traditional Yoga-training. It is rather due to a suscepti-
bility for the supranatural. "It is my experience," says Aurobindo, "that there is something beyond the human
mind. Man can reach higher perfection only by a higher
force which enters and takes over the total action of man.
The true superman is not a man who has climbed up to
his own natural zenith and not a higher degree of human
greatness, knowledge, power, will, character, genius, dynamic strength, sanctity, love, purity or perfection. The
supermind is something beyond mental man. It is a
higher consciousness than the highest consciousness peculiar to human nature. The human mind does not
change by itself. It only changes by opening itself to the
coming of the supermind, from which alone the transformation can emanate. Supramental man is only an instrument of the self-manifestation of God in the evolution of
humanity."[10]

Aurobindo himself did not intend to raise all humanity
to the level of the supramental. He rather wants to "establish," first of all, the supramental consciousness in
present humanity and then "introduce it into the consciousness of this world, to let it work and fulfill itself
there."

> For the leader of the way in a work like ours has
> not only to bring down or represent and embody the
> Divine, but to *represent too the ascending element
> in humanity* and *to bear the burden of humanity to
> the full*, and experience not in a mere play or Lila but
> in grim earnest, all the obstruction, difficulty, opposi-
> tion, baffled, hampered and only slowly victorious la-
> bor which are possible on the path. But it *is not nec-
> essary, not tolerable that all should be repeated over
> again to the full in the experience of others*. It is be-
> cause we have the complete experience that we can
> show a straighter and easier road to others—if they

will only consent to take it. *It is because of our own
experience* won at a tremendous price that we can
urge you and others to "Take the psychic attitude; follow the straight sunlit path, with the Divine openly
and secretly bearing you up—if secretly, he will yet
show himself in good time—do not insist on the hard,
hampered, roundabout, and difficult journey."[11]

It is this religious interpretation of the idea of evolution which makes the distinction from Darwin evident.
The monistic idea of evolution assumes a continuous
chain of mutations in order to prove the uninterrupted
development from the amoeba via the primate to man.
But, according to Aurobindo's experience, this development without lacunae, based on a compelling law of nature, does not exist. With the intervention of the supramental, something really new emerges, something that
never existed before, and cannot be derived from anything. This is the intervention of the supermind which
creates a new man with new senses and new capacities of
communication.

Aurobindo tirelessly describes the novelty of these capacities of supramental man. To a large extent, they are
identical with the faculties of extrasensory perception and
communication on which modern parapsychology has
tried to do research on the experimental level. In the area
of charismatic sanctity, they manifested themselves in
ever-changing outward form, as rare exceptions. There is
no doubt that Aurobindo himself gave rather impressive
proof of possessing such parapsychological faculties about
which people who knew him have given unimpeachable
testimony.

It will be easier for us to understand Aurobindo's aim
if we consider that he deals critically with Nietzsche when
explaining his own idea of the superman and the coming
of the supramental. Apparently he had read an English

translation of Nietzsche. This philosopher's concept of the superman was also evolutionary and he was therefore very close to Aurobindo. However, the distinction between him and Aurobindo gives an even clearer picture of the peculiar nature of the latter's concept.

Aurobindo sees Nietzsche as "the troubled, profound, half-luminous Hellenizing Slav[12] with his strange clarities, his violent half-ideas, his rare gleaming intuitions that come marked with the stamp of absolute truth and sovereignty of light." This judgment shows that Aurobindo has not denied a certain measure of recognition to his rival. In a way, he admits the kinship between his own conception and that of Nietzsche.

This kinship can be seen, first of all, in the outline of a progressive anthropology, a classifying of man within the scheme of evolution in which man in his present form appears as merely a transition from a lower to a higher stage of development. The second common concept is the eschatological interpretation of the idea of evolution. Both thinkers are convinced that the evolution of humanity in world history has now reached a point, in their own era, in which the evolutionary stage, represented by the superman, begins to emerge. Another common point between the two is the messianic self-interpretation, according to which both consider themselves the first representatives of this higher stage of evolution.[13]

Just because they agreed on so many points, Aurobindo felt it necessary to draw a very clear dividing-line between himself and Nietzsche. For he states that, in the final analysis, Nietzsche's ideas were merely "brilliant half-ideas," that he saw "only half the truth," and that he was "an apostle who never completely understood his own message." This means that, according to Aurobindo, Nietzsche has not penetrated to the pure concept of the superman. "But for the most part this message that had come to his inner hearing, vibrating out of a distant in-

finite like a strain caught from the lyre of far-off Gods, did
get, in his effort to appropriate and make it nearer to him,
mixed up with a somewhat turbulent surge of collateral
ideas that drowned much of the pure original note."[14]

And what is that imperfection, impurity, and incom-
pleteness in Nietzsche's concept of the superman? Aurobindo points out that "the deity within may confront us
either with the clear, joyous and radiant countenance of
the God or the stern convulsed visage of the Titan."[15]
He blames Nietzsche for only showing the stern features
of the Titan when painting the picture of the superman:
"He presents to us a superman who fiercely and arro-
gantly repels the burden of sorrow and service, not one
who arises victorious over mortality and suffering, his ascension vibrant with the triumph song of liberated humanity."

Aurobindo thus opposes his own "radiant" image of
the superman, which is characterized by a victory over
mortality and suffering, to Nietzsche's "titanic" and
"stern" supermanhood, which "simply tries to get rid of
the encumbrances of effort and service instead of fighting
to overcome them . . . To lose the link of nature's moral
evolution is a capital fault in the apostle of supermanhood." It is Nietzsche's arrogant attack of morals which
proves to Aurobindo that he has missed the point of the
true idea of supermanhood, which can only be born in
"the bosom of a humanity long tested, ripened, and puri-
fied by the fire of egotistical and altruistic suffering."[16]
And Aurobindo continues:

> Who is the *superman*? He who can rise above this
> matter-regarding, broken, mental human unit and
> possess himself universalized and deified in a divine
> force, a divine love and joy and a divine knowledge.
> If thou keepest this limited human ego and think-
> est thyself the *superman*, thou art but the fool of thy

own pride, the plaything of thy own force and the instrument of thy own illusions.

Nietzsche saw the *superman* as the lion soul passing out of camelhood, but the true heraldic device and token of the *superman* is the lion seated upon the camel which stands upon the cow of plenty. If thou canst not be the slave of all mankind thou art not fit to be its master, and if thou canst not make thy nature as Vasishtha's cow of plenty with all mankind to draw its wish from her udders, what avails thy leonine *supermanhood?*

Be to the world as the lion in fearlessness and lordship, as the camel in patience and service, as the cow in quiet, forbearing and maternal beneficence. Raven on all the joys of God as a lion over its prey, but bring also all humanity into that infinite field of luxurious ecstasy to wallow there and to pasture.[17]

As the cause of Nietzsche's one-sided, titanic interpretation of the superman, Aurobindo mentions, with deep insight, Nietzsche's "hostile prejudice against the Christidea of the crucified God and its consequences," and the adoption of incomplete Greek ideas of the superman. Compared to Nietzsche, the Hindu appears here as an apologist of Christianity. He also defends the Christian concept of the suffering and self-humiliation of Christ as the only condition of raising man to the level of the superhuman.

But Aurobindo is not a defender of supermanhood who conceives the image of God as the antithesis *per se* of the titanic. He rather suggests that, in a true superman, the titanic must be overcome and canceled out by the divine. Speaking of his image of supermanhood he says: "Certainly, power is included." For him, too, "to be the divine man is to be self-ruler and world-ruler." But this element of sovereignty which is a condition of supermanhood demands "that the ego must be crucified, and how shall men consent to this if God and the gods have not shown them the way?"

Nietzsche's superman who interprets his superman-hood in a one-sided way, in the titanic sense, merely calls for "a visible, tangible mastery and a sensational domina-tion." "The Titan would unify by devouring, not by har-monizing; he must conquer and trample what is not him-self either out of existence or into subservience so that his own image may stand out stamped upon all things and dominating all his environment."[18]

In true supermanhood, however, this titanic arrogance has been overcome. Aurobindo describes it as "a certain divine and harmonious extract from all that is essential in man." Aurobindo's ideas thus come close to the specula-tions of Jacob Boehme on androgynous original man[19] and to the Adam Kadmon of the Cabala.[20] The fact that man was created in the image of God is the foundation for his supermanhood. This image of God aspires to its finite, pure, and perfect realization in the superman. Thus man himself is "nature's great term of transition in which she grows conscious of her aim; in him she looks up from the animal with open eyes toward her divine ideal."

But this ideal is not the one-sided manifestation of one single divine quality, as love or power, but the harmony and unity of powers, of "the names of God." If all those powers, names, and gods "are founded together on a soul of sacrifice that lives in unity with all the world and ac-cepts all things to transmute them, then is the condition of man's integral self-transcendence reached. This and not a haughty, strong, and prideful egoistic self-culture en-throning itself upon an enslaved humanity is the divine way of supermanhood."[21]

Aurobindo blames Nietzsche's anti-Christian attitude as the cause for his lack of understanding of the super-man concept. But despite this explicit criticism, Aurobindo's image of the superman is not a return to the charismatic image of the superman as we find it in the theology of the early Church. In the end, he considers Christ as just one of the manifestations of the divine in the history of mankind, as one of the avatars who led the process of evolution of humanity forward on the road to a higher form of existence, namely, supermanhood.

But in spite of this, he has understood and established what is essential in the figure of Christ: The self-realization of God is reached through its opposite, the self-renunciation, the crucifixion of the ego. It could even be said that Aurobindo has christianized the entire traditional Hindu concept of the avatars by his view of the figure of Christ. He raised the cross and the crown of thorns to symbols of avatardom. "The gods work oftenest veiled by light or by the stormdrift; they do not disdain to live among men, even in the garb of the herdsman or the artisan; they do not shrink from the cross and the crown of thorns either in their inner evolution or their outward fortunes . . . To take all that is essential in the human being and uplift it to its most absolute term, so that it may become an element of light, joy, power for oneself and others, this is divinity. This, too, should be the drift of supermanhood."[22]

Aurobindo's image of the superman thus absorbs the Christian concept of man. But it goes further than just looking at the cross, death, and suffering. It considers them as mere stages by which the boundaries of present human existence are overcome and from which the higher stage of supermanhood is then supposed to emerge. On this basis, we can understand the sentence which I saw on the wall over the door when I first stepped into my guest room at the Aurobindo Ashram and which puzzled me thereafter: "It is not a crucified body but a glorified body that overcomes the evil of the world."

By including this Christian understanding of self-

restraint in his concept of supermanhood, Aurobindo
has indeed overcome the characteristic one-sidedness of
Nietzsche's human image. Nietzsche actually replaced the
new image of man by a convulsively anti-Christian Christology.

Aurobindo's superman-idea is closely tied to his own
religious consciousness and to his consciousness of carrying out a mission. It is also connected with the doctrine
of evolution of Western natural science, with the Hindu
avatar theory, and with Western Christology. Its result
was that Indian Christians also dealt with the problem of
finding a positive relationship between scientific anthropology and the Christian image of man and expectation
of the end of time.

This attempt was made, in a very impressive way, in
Madras by Sri P. Chenchiah, M.L., who died a few years
ago. He was the spiritual leader of a group of Indian
Christians of various denominations who try to understand the Christian revelation with the criteria of the
Indian Yoga tradition. His thoughts are expressed in a
very important treatise entitled *The Destiny of Man and
the Interpretation of History.*[23]

On the basis of his personal experiences, this Indian layman has given new validity to an essential element of the
early Christian evangelical image of man: The redemption of man is a creative act of the Holy Ghost, who initiates the process of higher development and perfection of
man. An urge toward perfection is at work in present man
and tends to raise him above his present level.

Chenchiah also sees the evolution of man in a great,
universal connection with the development of the *regnum
animale*. Creation is not something finite and completed.
It is the medium for an ever-clearer self-revelation of the
Creator in his work. Chenchiah is conscious of the "artist
behind creation" whose creative imagination is realized in
a surprising series of newer and higher self-manifestations.

This work of divine self-manifestation is aimed at perfection. The divine artist who has set evolution into motion wants to complete it too. "The artist behind evolution cannot be satisfied with less than perfection."

By this understanding of creation as a progressive self-manifestation of God, Chenchiah finds a new access to an understanding of Jesus Christ. He feels that with Jesus a new humanity and a new stage of human existence begins. "His disciples considered him Tathagata—he that is to come, the one who carries human destiny to new heights." Peter's acknowledgment of Jesus as the Christ, the son of the living God, is an acknowledgment to the one who transcends the destiny of man. The saying that "the Kingdom of God is among you" means "that in him the supra-life has entered into the conditions of the world and has begun to operate on man and nature."

With Jesus, a new and perfect type of man therefore entered into world history, opening a new phase in human annals, a new stage of human existence on the road to perfection. Jesus is the "new man," the "second Adam," representing a new and higher human life. He appears in history as the result of a creative act of mutation brought about by the Spirit. What comes to the fore in him is "a new vitality and an abundance of life expressing itself in healing. Morality has assumed a new form in him." "He brings into the biological stream a new cosmic power-personality, the Holy Spirit . . . It descends on man and transforms him from the very roots—body, mind, and soul . . ."

The essential novelty of the new type of man which emerges with Jesus is, first of all, "a spiritual body and a new control over nature. Spirit triumphs over life just as mind conquered life." The resurrection of Jesus was not a one-time miracle, but a necessity of this new manifestation of life. The first manifestation occurs in him, but the new life continues. The essential feature of this new human existence is the consciousness of God, the certainty that God is part of one's being. Jesus thus appears as the "prototype of a new species of humanity," as the first of a new stage in the evolution from man to superman. Chenchiah finds repeatedly, at this point, that there is a remarkable agreement between Christian anthropology and the concept of evolution in natural science.

In connection with this, Chenchiah also discovers the inner connection between the old Christian anthropology and Aurobindo's image of man. Aurobindo proceeds from the conviction that present man is obviously imperfect. This specific imperfection of man in his present state points by itself to a higher goal of evolution, "a higher life with better faculties." Seen from this viewpoint, Christian eschatology appears to be the vision and divination of a future higher stage of human evolution at which its present shortcomings will be overcome. The future goal will then be reached, of which we can only have a foreboding in our present situation of limited existence and understanding.

According to Chenchiah's opinion, Aurobindo's anthropology is aimed at the "advent" of supramental life which represents exactly that stage which is called the "coming of the Holy Spirit" in the Christian promise. "Nearly twenty centuries after Jesus and St. Paul, India produced the best interpreter of his incarnation from within Hinduism. He preaches that supramental life is at hand and has even entered life impinging upon us, seeking embodiment in us and working toward the creation of a new race of supermen, the Christian sons of God, the incarnate God-men."

Jesus was the prototype of God's self-manifestation. Nietzsche's superman was a titanic fighter against God. Aurobindo's superman is the new man, fashioned in the image of God, the new stage of man's evolution. In the person of Aurobindo, the new man has become reality in human history. As a Christian, Chenchiah therefore consciously admits and accepts Sri Aurobindo's self-interpretation as the Messiah. "The new man, the divine race, already exists among us."

Aurobindo is thus included in the Christian history of salvation. This is not done simply in the way a sectarian would do it, namely, by replacing the returning Christ in the Christian history of salvation by the figure of Aurobindo. Aurobindo is not understood as the final goal on the road of evolution of the supramental, but as a further step on the road to a progressive self-realization of Christ in human history. He is a link in the chain of the manifestations of the "Christ of Evolution," to use the term of Teilhard de Chardin, whose concept of the supramental appears to show in many points a striking inner connection with Aurobindo's.

A Christian outside India could hardly support this interpretation which gives Aurobindo such a high place in the history of salvation. But the idea still shows to what extent Indian thought was permeated spontaneously by the idea of evolution. This does not only apply to the ideological, theoretical concept. New charismatic types of men were also created, and so was a new model for the education of future man.

XII

The Ideas of Teilhard de Chardin on the Origin and Goal of Man

It will be only fair if we devote the last two chapters to that natural scientist and theologian who has presented to our time the most widely discussed interpretation of creation and the end of time, namely, Teilhard de Chardin.[1]

The spiritual development of Teilhard de Chardin is deeply influenced by the tension between natural science and theology. Let us look first at Teilhard's career as a natural scientist: He was born on May 1, 1881, at Sarcenat, near Clermont, in the Auvergne. A geologist and paleontologist by profession, he worked in these fields as a member of the Jesuit Order, which he joined in 1899, and as an ordained priest.

His training as a natural scientist led him from a professorship in physics in Cairo (1908) to geological and paleontological research in England. After his ordination as a priest in 1911, he was employed by the Musée d'Histoire Naturelle in Paris. After the end of the war, he became professor of geology at the Institut Catholique in Paris.

The period of his great journeys of exploration began in 1923 with a trip to Central China. In 1928, he went on a mission in French Somaliland and Ethiopia. In 1929, he returned to China where he did special research on the Sinanthropus that had been discovered by Davidson Black and Bohlin. He was appointed scientific adviser to the Chinese Service of Geological Survey, and in 1930, participated in an American expedition to Central Asia. In

1931–32 he was selected as the geologist of the Haardt-Citroën expedition. He participated in the so-called Yellow Crusade which consisted of two columns of explorers who traversed Central Asia in various directions, using special Citroën caterpillar-driven vehicles. With an American expedition, he traveled through Northern India in 1935–36 and through Burma the following year.

Cut off from Europe by the events of World War II, he lived in China from 1939–46 where he experienced all phases of the political development until the victory of the Red Army. After a short stay in Paris, where he was appointed member of the Académie des Sciences in 1950, he proceeded to South Africa to organize paleontological excavations. He then accepted a position in New York with the American Foundation for Anthropological Research, the Wenner-Gren Foundation, which sent him on a second mission to South Africa in 1953. He died in New York on Easter Sunday, April 10, 1955.[2]

This is the outward and professional aspect of his career, showing an explorer's life of unusual productivity. Teilhard is one of the few men who explored the geological and paleoanthropological structure of Asia, Indonesia, and Africa, covering areas which, up to that time, were still represented by white spots on the map. His work as an explorer was carried out under circumstances of truly heroic self-denial and under the most dangerous climatic and political conditions. His valuable findings, discoveries and insights enriched knowledge about the paleontological development of the animal kingdom, the hominids, and the first human races.

But there is another side. As a theologian and a priest, his geological and paleontological research was of interest to him in getting a comprehensive view of the development of life from the first movement in the atomic structure, the *prévie*, until the formation of man. He wanted to get a total view of the genesis and future of humanity in the context of the genesis and organization of life in the universe. The decisive point for him was the unrelenting intellectual effort to find a synopsis of his geological, physical, paleontological, and paleoanthropological understanding in relation to a new *Christian vision of the universe and of man,* or to put it more precisely, of the future perfection of the universe in man. "True science is the science of the future, which will gradually be implemented through life."[3] "The world is only interesting if you look at its future."[4] What he had in mind was a new interpretation of the Christian message. The findings of modern natural science, of the creative and organizing forces of the universe, of the development of life, the origin of species, the genesis of man should contribute toward a new and fuller understanding of the Christian message of salvation and the coming of the Kingdom of God. In fact, they should find their fulfillment and most profound meaning in the Christian message. The history of the evolution of life culminates in the christification of the universe.

He found deep understanding among friends who had similar views and among scientists and intellectuals. But the representatives of the traditional, official theology of the Thomist type did not agree with him at all. The leaders of his Order, in particular, increasingly opposed his tendency to integrate his scientific knowledge with theology. In fact, they prohibited what would have been closest to his heart: the publication of his writings, in which he outlined the new Christian view of his anthropological findings, and the creation of a broader circle of students by his personal work as teacher and lecturer in Paris. The imprimatur of his ecclesiastical superiors was given only for the publication of his purely scientific, anthropological or paleontological explorations in learned journals with a very low circulation. His systematic writings, in which he outlined a picture of the total development of the "human phenomenon," never received the imprimatur, although he revised the manuscripts repeatedly, as in the case of his principal work *Le phénomène humain*, in order to take care of the objections raised in Rome.[5]

His lecturing activities were approved only for small circles of scientists. Any far-reaching activity, especially among academic youth or the younger generation of theologians, was prohibited. Thus, in 1923, he had to abandon his chair at the Institut Catholique, the Roman Catholic theological faculty in Paris. After having been in China for six years during World War II, his friends saw to it that, upon his return, a vacant chair of the Collège de France was offered to him. This was the highest recognition and token of distinction for his work. But his superiors in Rome did not allow him to accept this chair, which would have been the fulfillment of all his wishes; they allowed him, however, to undertake new journeys of exploration in South Africa. On his return from South Africa, he found in New York that his superiors still refused to agree to the resumption of his activity in Paris, and he, therefore, accepted a permanent position in New York.

This tension had an influence on his literary work, as it is available now. As stated before, only his strictly scientific, geological and paleontological research was published in his lifetime. Most of his other essays and lectures were not printed, but were circulated privately in hectographed pamphlets and typewritten copies.

His collected works were not published until after his death, and then, too, in an unusual way. The imprimatur could not be obtained, and an unprotected edition of his writings, the publication of which had been so stubbornly prevented by the church hierarchy, was hardly feasible. Such a publication could only be pushed through by mobilizing prominent international scientists and men of letters as well as influential private circles. Accordingly, two committees were formed under the patronage of Her Majesty Queen Marie-José of Italy. The directors of the most important international geological, paleontological, and archeological research institutes and museums belonged to a committee of thirty-six scientists, among them Sir Julian Huxley and Sir Arnold J. Toynbee. There was also a *comité général* consisting of Teilhard's friends, among them writers and poets of world renown like Georges Duhamel, André Malraux, André Siegfried, and twenty-seven other personalities of equal weight and prestige.

Under the patronage of these two committees, the collected works of Teilhard were then published in Paris. So far, they consist of eight volumes, without imprimatur. We believe that this is the first time in modern history that such an international scientific and intellectual elite was mobilized successfully against the threat of official action by Rome.

But to this day the tension has not yet been relieved. Since Teilhard's death, a great deal of literature has been published by his supporters. They aggravated the situation with schoolboy-like exaggerations, raising their teacher and master to the level of a "Thomas Aquinas of the twentieth century," or of an inaugurator of a "Copernican change in the Christian understanding of the world." The Papal Theological Academy in Rome opposed these tendencies with remarkable severity. A special 1959 issue of its journal *Divinitas* is devoted to a critique of Teilhard de Chardin. Five leading Catholic theologians, members of the Papal Academy, refer to the fact that, by papal order, their academy has the task of defending the inviolable truth of the faith. They make an effort to prove that Teilhard de Chardin is ignorant of theology. He has introduced criteria and concepts of natural science into theology, thus creating confusion and instigating a dangerous seduction of the faithful.[6] The official judgment of the Sacrum Officium, dated June 30, 1962, uses similar arguments, both against Teilhard's doctrine and against his supporters who spread his serious "errors."[7]

This is the situation we must keep in mind in order to realize that there is indeed a great mind at work here. He outlines a new interpretation of the truth of the Christian faith, based on the new knowledge which natural science has gained about the "earth." This leads to considerable tensions with the traditional neo-Thomist interpretation of the Christian faith in the Roman Church. These tensions still continue to this day.

However, the study of Teilhard de Chardin's lifework is fraught with rather considerable difficulties. He has become fashionable in wide circles nowadays, but, frequently, people talk and write about him rather nonchalantly. It is therefore necessary, first of all, to point out the practical difficulties.

The first one is that, to this day, a critical edition of Teilhard's works does not exist. There is an edition of his collected works, to which we referred before, and which was published under the patronage of the abovementioned committees. But despite the array of prominent international scientists, this is not a scientific edition, particularly because it always gives just one version of Teilhard's works. It is known, however, that Teilhard revised his principal works repeatedly and very thoroughly. Various handwritten versions are still in existence. They are held by the appropriate church authorities, by friends, by the Teilhard Archive in Paris and by the Jesuit Order, which took over Teilhard's estate a day after his death. The available edition, however, does not indicate which version of the text was used nor how the published version differs from former or later revisions. We may be right in assuming that the most orthodox version was used for publication. However, the edition of the principal works in French reflects the taste and the theological attitude of the editors.

Among the writings of Teilhard which have been published, only two are complete works with their own titles chosen by the author: *Le phénomène humain* and *L'apparition de l'homme*. All others are collections of special essays and treatises by Teilhard which were published under general titles chosen by his posthumous editors and not by Teilhard himself. This applies, for example, to *Die Aktivation der Energie* or to *Die Zukunft des Menschen* (German translations of *L'activation de l'énergie* and *L'avenir de l'homme*). These essays and treatises appeared over several decades in a variety of journals or were distributed in hectographed form by his friends and followers. These collections were not arranged and not even planned by Teilhard in their present form. They are the result of a selection made by the editor after the author's death. It also appears that often dogmatic considerations and points of view were the decisive criteria for the selection and arrangement of the publication. Our basic attitude must therefore be critical as long as a critical edition of his collected works is not available, an attitude that applies even to the so-called original edition in French.

There are two factors which make the understanding of Teilhard particularly difficult from the standpoint of philological criticism. As a thinker who tried to reconcile his scientific knowledge with the convictions of his faith, Teilhard de Chardin has, in the first place, created his own terminological language which is highly unconventional. In the language which he uses to present his mysticism and his theological world view, he makes surprisingly little use of the traditional terms of official Thomist theology. He rather introduces into theology a number of categories of natural science to which he gives an entirely new spiritual meaning. Even his prayers are full of new concepts. They take a high degree of knowledge of natural science for granted. Some of them use the terminology of treatises on physics or biology such as *granulation, planetisation, phylum, enroulement,* etc.[8]

Besides, he has introduced a number of surprising new creations of theological terms. Their formation follows the same rule by which new, abstract terms are formed in natural science, out of Greek or Latin roots. These new words give to his theological language the charm of a technological, scientific modernism, or even supermodernism. As an analogy to terms taken from physics, such as *ionisation,* he forms the term *amorisation* (from *amour*), by which he means that socialization, which exerts pressure to bring about the uniformity of mankind, should be penetrated progressively by love. Besides *amorisation,* other terms are found in a theological context such as *planetisation, corpusculisation, internisation, hominisation, cephalisation, cerebralisation* or *cerebration.* Each term is also part of a network of correlated terms and has certain connotations and secondary accents. It reminds us of analogous terms of the physical world and the world of animals.

What German authors have published about Teilhard so far usually does not go beyond superficial information and rather terse criticism. The French sources are often completely ignored. However, German critical scientific Teilhard research, based on a knowledge of the original works in French, is now in progress.[9] Meanwhile, the publication of Teilhard's works has progressed rapidly, and literature on him by both French and English experts is available. But the task is difficult. By his education and intellect, Teilhard stands completely outside the traditions of German philosophical and spiritual history. Even in terminology, there are therefore few points of contact with German spiritual traditions. A number of his ideas, however, have an affinity with the ideas of the philosophy of nature and philosophy of history developed by Hegel, Schelling, and Franz von Baader, although the works of these philosophers were completely unknown to him.

We can say that Teilhard's purpose in theology was the attempt to integrate the Christian understanding of the history of salvation into the total movement of evolution. This means, in effect, that the history of salvation is extended to the total development of life and, indeed, to the universe. The evolution of life culminates in man, who is the real axis of evolution. What happens in Teilhard's anthropology is actually a reversal of the interpretation of man given by many materialistic disciples of Darwin.

Teilhard has restored man's axial position within the sequence of evolution by showing that man is the organic continuation of that "rolling in" process which has taken place within the kingdom of living creatures—the biosphere—since the first living being emerged and was actually indicated in the organization of matter.

It was the main purpose of Teilhard's scientific research to find the manner of development of emerging life and the evolution of the *phénomène humain*.

Man initiates a new phase of life. Man is a thinking creature. The animal knows, but man alone knows that he knows. It can no longer be determined in what manner man first gained this consciousness. Within its development we notice, however, a considerable shifting of the point of gravity. Man first used the faculties of his consciousness in order to live, to survive. Today we live in order to think, to partake of the entire fullness of our consciousness. "We are carried by a progressive wave of consciousness."[10]

Where will humanity be carried by this wave? Thinking humanity, as a whole, is in the midst of an irresistible process for which Teilhard uses various terms. Sometimes he calls it "socialization," sometimes "totalization," sometimes "collective human genesis," then again "super-reflection," or "rolling in and converging of men." He also uses such terms as "development of a superconsciousness" and, very frequently, "superman"—*surhomme*.

Teilhard points out tirelessly that certain developments of mankind evidently are approaching their conclusion now. The first indication of this is the urge for uniformity and socialization. Teilhard considers socialization as the essential element in the process of evolution. "Socialization" is the organic extension into the human area of the mutual attraction of the atoms which we already find in the lifeless universe. In the animal kingdom, the urge for connection and union is solidified and refined immensely. Finally, within the noosphere—the area of self-consciousness—we observe the capacity of man to submerge ever more consciously into a steadily enlarged milieu of collectivity. "If socialization is nothing but a higher effect of 'body-formation'—*corpusculisation*—then the noosphere, as the last and highest product of this process, can get full and decisive meaning only under *one* condition: if it is considered, to its full extent, as one single infinite body in which, after more than six hundred million years, the work of forming the brain—*cerebration*—is completed in the biosphere."[11]

This process of socialization takes place on all levels today. It can be seen in the technological and economic uniformity of the world and in the uniformity of social structures. It manifests itself as a process of meeting and mutual penetration of civilizations and cultures on a global scale. It takes place with a breathtaking acceleration made possible by modern technological methods of communication and transportation. Humanity is beginning to organize in a manner which was hitherto unimaginable. It is combined into new supergroups which, in turn, are getting intertwined into new superunits and superbrains.

Simultaneously, humanity has reached the limits of its physical expansion. The earth is populated. It can no longer obey the law of "neolithic patriarchalism" which asked men to "multiply."[12] Within the noosphere, over-pressure—*surcompression*—has built up on our globe. The conditions for a new jump in evolution have developed, which will raise humanity into the sphere of the ultra-human.

Human totalization, the technical and social standardization of our life, bears in itself the danger of mechanization and dehumanization. But since it originates in man, its true character is that of a biologically new dimension. The *compression* which leads to totalization is a spiritual phenomenon and one which generates spirit. It leads to ever-stronger *personalization*. This is perhaps the boldest and most controversial conclusion in his reasoning.

"The laws of biogenesis (the genesis of life) naturally lead to an economic improvement of the human situation. But what is involved is not well-being (*bien-être*), but the hunger for being-more (*plus-être*) which alone can save thinking humanity from the *taedium vitae*, the tedium of life."[13] To-be-more means to explore more, to know more, to understand more, to unite more, to love more.

This is the point where a new decisive line of Teilhard's thinking begins. Up to now, we looked from behind, as it were, at evolution, the further rolling-in process and the compression of the noosphere. We saw it from the angle of the biological pressure of evolution which presses humanity together on our planet and forces it into standardization. This pressure is, in actual fact, a pull forward which originates in the goal itself where all lines of development converge. "It is necessary that all men of the earth should first reach the terminal point of their evolutionary growth. This is a physical prerequisite. Then it will be discovered that the perfection which lies beyond the human—*l'achèvement ultra-humain*—which neo-Humanism foresees in evolution, is identical with the summit-point which all Christians expect under the term 'incarnation.' "[14]

The perfection of the earth thus corresponds to the "perfection of God" in the visible world. This means that for Teilhard the genesis of the Kingdom of God, the incarnation, will not occur as the sudden irruption of something supernatural into a degraded world ruled by demons. It will rather be the ascent of the earth and its metamorphosis into a reality which has hitherto hardly been recognized. This is a reality of "a completely different kind," the point Omega, in which the noosphere will reach its summit-point of uniformity. Uniform humanity will flow into God, while God as the center and axis, flows into humanity and will become visible in it.[15]

But there is one point which we must not overlook. Humanity is not understood as detached from the earth and the universe. As the "spiritual earth" it is that species into which the ascent and transformation of life, from the *prévie* to the biosphere, and from there to the noosphere, are compressed.

The incarnation of God is not a process which exhausts itself in a single and unique historical person. It is a process of transformation which aims at the divinization of man. But, in man, it transforms the entire universe.

We see that an entirely new understanding of God is at work here. No longer is there a God above who grasps a world which is running away from him. But there is a *Dieu en-avant*,[16] a God ahead of us, who realizes himself in his creation. He is the future goal of the world and of mankind. In him, the entire evolution of life converges and he directs this evolution toward himself.[17]

Here the main Christian root of Teilhard's speculations becomes clearly apparent. Incarnation is the basic idea of his scientific and theological thinking, the element which joins natural science and theology. He recognizes the creation of man as the basic urge in the organization of the universe, the axis of the basic forward-movement of life. All matter wants to live, all life wants to become man, and in man, it wants to join man's goal, which is God. Incarnation is the aim of God, the aim of his self-unfolding and self-realization.

On this basis, the understanding of Christ also receives an entirely new aspect. For Teilhard, too, the historical Jesus Christ is the personal epiphany of a God whose work is visible in evolution while he is not himself visible. God becomes visible in the form of a historical human personality. Incarnation in Jesus Christ, however, is not a unique historical process, but the beginning of a new phase of evolution, of a new form of life, of a new manner of existence. Mankind will be included in this process, in proportion to its spiritualization, personification, and christianization. Teilhard therefore frequently refers to the "greater Christ"[18] or the "Christ of Evolution."[19] By these terms, he means the Christ who is the personal goal of incarnation, in whom the incarnation of the universe and the incarnation of God converge. In the future, humanity and the universe will become part of him to an increasing degree. On this basis, we can also understand why the previously described process of unification is referred to as personification. Personification is "christification."

In 1936, Teilhard wrote from China: "I believe that I have never before seen my vocation to personalize the world in God so clearly and so detached from everything."[20] And in 1937, he wrote: "The universe converges toward the Person."[21] For man, this process happens as the process of a transformation in Christ.

This greater Christ is the "focal point, not only of individual and 'supernatural' redemption, but also of collective and earthly salvation. All this is combined and realized in the countenance of the universal Christ."[22]

The universe itself is, like man, on the road to christification. Teilhard therefore refers to his faith as "the total, generalized confidence which flows together with active devotion to a universe which is on the way to christification."[23] The greater Christ thus appears as the inner axis and the goal in the process to hominize the universe. Thus Teilhard can actually refer to a christification of evolution.

XIII

A Theological Criticism of Teilhard de Chardin

The main difficulty for a critique of the ideas of Teilhard de Chardin is the fact that the literature available at the present time was mostly written by Teilhard's *friends*. They are dominated by the intense desire to show Teilhard, on the one hand, as a unique thinker, as a trailblazer of a new theological vision of Christian revelation, as the initiator of an entirely new epoch of theological thinking. On the other hand, they want to acquit him of all indictments of dogmatic errors and to reduce to a harmless minimum the charges raised against him by the official Church.

The claim of the uniqueness of Teilhard's ideas cannot, however, be maintained. It is said that he has used the idea of evolution, in a positive sense, for a theological interpretation of the Christian image of man and the Christian history of salvation. The remark of Friedrich Heer referring to him as the "Thomas Aquinas of the twentieth century"[1] is not only an exaggeration but also materially wrong. Teilhard's visions cannot be systematized in a Scholastic way. It must also be called an exaggeration if Heimo Dolch compares the present official opposition of Rome against Teilhard de Chardin with the negative attitude of the Church against Aristotle. In connection with the *Monitum* of the Holy Office against Teilhard Dolch writes as follows: "Historians of philosophy remember the bans against Aristotle in the thirteenth century. Many of them were issued, but they remained without effect. The acceptance of Aristotle gained ground with irresistible impetus."[2] Here we have to comment, too, that a comparison of Teilhard's intuitions with the precise logic of Aristotelian thinking is mistaken.

Considering the history of theology in the nineteenth and twentieth centuries we can, however, make the following observations: If Teilhard undertook (as he actually did) to deal with the doctrine of evolution as a theologian and to develop a new conspectus of understanding in the fields of theology and natural science, he is a European latecomer and straggler. He is just catching up, in the field of Catholic theology, with a task which Anglo-Saxon and North American theology performed immediately after the appearance of Darwin and of the philosophers and natural scientists under Darwin's influence. It was carried out with great care and thoroughness. German Protestant theology has also dealt with it since the beginning of the twentieth century.

As we have already shown to some extent (in chapter IX of this book), there is not a single idea of Teilhard's which had not already been raised in the theological discussion at the turn of the century. This statement does not say anything about the rank of his ideas nor about their value for us today. But it helps to clarify his position within the total development of modern theology and in the meeting and confrontation of theology with modern natural science. It also protects us from overrating him improperly.

It appears to me that his importance can be seen in three particular points.

(1) The knowledge of the structure of the world, of matter, and of the biosphere has been deepened and widened immeasurably since the time when theologians with serious scientific knowledge dealt with the problem of evolution. Thus correlations of a uniform structure of

the universe in decisive sections which were only surmised at the end of the last century or at the beginning
of the present one can now be perceived much more
clearly than previously, as, for instance, in the time of
Schelling. The progress of modern natural science in the
fields of atom research, cell biology, virus research, has
brought links to light which could not be recognized
previously. The same applies particularly to anthropology. Paleoanthropology, modern brain-research, the exploration of the primates, have brought entirely new
connections to light.

From the standpoint of museum technique, surprising
progress has also been made. Previously, the few finds of
pre-hominids and paleoanthropoi eked out a miserable
existence in the storerooms of museums. Now they have
a central position in descriptions and observations. Knowing about the main finds has become part of general
education. By the application of entirely new methods on
the determination of relative periods of time, research on
prehistory and early history has allowed us to see connections of historical development in periods which, only a
few decades ago, were completely outside any consideration in historical terms.

Teilhard was a paleoanthropologist and biologist by
profession. In this field, too, his importance has been
exaggerated by his followers in many cases. The *homo
pekinensis* was not discovered but merely described by
him. On the occasion of the one hundredth anniversary
of the publication of Darwin's principal work, a three-
volume collection of articles on evolution was published
in Chicago with contributions of leading biologists and
anthropologists from all over the world, but particularly
from the United States and Britain. Teilhard's name is
not mentioned in any of the treatises on natural science
which deal with evolution in general and the problem of
the genesis of man in particular.[3]

As a recognized expert, supported by the latest findings of biology and paleoanthropology, Teilhard could still oppose, within the field of Catholic theology, a verdict which was obsolete for a long time. As part of an anti-modernist campaign, it condemned the doctrine of evolution as bearing a kind of joint guilt with freethinkers, freemasons, supporters of cremation, and communists. A man of lesser expert knowledge and international reputation among the scholars of his field would not have been able to break down this wall of traditional dogmatic prejudices.

(2) The second special element in the theology of evolution, as developed by Teilhard de Chardin, is very evident. It is rather strange that this has never been stated in Germany and that a Protestant theologian had to express it. For Teilhard de Chardin, the original image of evolution is the transformation of the material part of the elements into the body and blood of Christ through the Mass. The transformation which matter undergoes by proceeding from the first to the highest stage of evolution, the stage of christification, is represented mystically and subsequently executed sacramentally by the Mass. It was the steady, daily inspiration by his priestly office through carrying out the sacrament of the Mass which inspired Teilhard's theological thinking. In ever new visions, he sensed the link between the christification taking place in the universe and the process of the sacramental transformation of matter.

The transformation of the elements of bread and wine into the body and blood of Christ is the mystery, experienced anew every day, which appears to him as the model of evolution of the entire universe and of the total development of life between Alpha and Omega. In the end, the lines of evolution of the universe itself, matter which coalesces into ever-higher stages, converges eventually into the one spiritual-corporeal, universal person-

ality of the cosmic Christ. The transformation in the
Mass is for him a process, experienced anew every day, of
anticipation, condensation, and mystical representation
of that universal world-process which runs its course in
the immense periods of aeons between the points Alpha
and Omega. It is an ascent and a transformation of matter taking place during the ascent by which the christification of the world is accomplished, unfolding itself
through the biosphere and the noosphere and emerging
out of matter. Evolution is identical with the *eucharis-
tisation* of the universe, the transformation of the cosmos into the body of Christ.

The most profound elucidation of the links between
his understanding of the Eucharist and his concept of
evolution is given in his "Mass on the Altar of the World."
This is a Eucharistic prayer which Teilhard conceived in
a situation in which he had neither altar, nor bread, nor
wine to celebrate Mass. His life repeatedly brought him
into such situations, once when he was a soldier in
World War I at the front in the Aisne valley, and another
time in the steppes of Central Asia during one of his ex-
peditions of exploration. The text of this Mass was circulated for a long time in private and typewritten copies.
Only now has it been published in the most recently
issued volume of his works, *Hymn of the Universe.*[4]

Since once again, Lord—though this time not in
the Aisne forests, but in the steppes of Asia—I have
neither bread, nor wine, nor altar, I will raise myself
beyond these symbols up to the pure majesty of the
Real itself; and I, your priest, will make the whole
earth my altar and on it offer you all the labors and
sufferings of the world. . . .

Receive, O Lord, this all-embracing Host which
your whole Creation, moved by your magnetism, offers you at this dawn of a new day. This bread, our

toil, is of itself, I know, but an immense fragmenta-
tion; this wine, our pain, is no more, I know, than a
draught that dissolves. Yet, in the very depths of this
formless mass, you have implanted—and this I am
sure of, for I sense it—a desire, irresistible and hal-
lowing, which makes us cry out, believer and unbe-
liever alike: 'Lord, make us *one.*'

(3) But it appears to me that his main importance lies
in the fact that he opened again the dimension of hope
for our time. The opening of the theological aspect of the
theory of evolution occurred at a time when the world, or
at least the European and American world, got tired of
existentialism and theological dialectics. This turning
back to the analysis of one's own existence, this scorpion-
like contortion of the poisonous sting against oneself,
this flirting with evil, this digging in the unfathomable
depths of one's own being, has led to a petrifaction of
thinking.

Without a doubt, there is some justification for Teilhard's charge that our time is "hypnotized by evil." The
generation of thinkers who came to the fore after World
War II suffered the fate of Lot's wife. She looked back
upon burning Sodom and Gomorrah. She could not look
away from the picture of decline and destruction. She
became mesmerized by the abyss of human aberrations,
by sexual, social, and spiritual abnormalities which led
to the destruction of Sodom. Her imagination became
engrossed in contemplating the bedrooms, singed by a
rain of sulphur, the dens of usury and vice. She got lost
in the constricting numbness of fear and defeat and—she
was converted into stone.

Daniélou writes about Teilhard: "One of the great
diseases of the modern mind is the 'enjoyment' of misfortune, the *'goût du malheur.'* Teilhard detests this with
all his heart. And he is right. I wish it were possible to

eliminate forever these poisonous miasmas of a decadent Western intelligentsia!"[5]

A new generation has emerged today, which is getting tired of having its life poisoned by people like Kierkegaard, whose human failure in coping with the simplest problems of life and insufficiency for life drove them into devious dialectics. They have discovered that the "revolt" by which everything real is being questioned has become an empty formula and is, therefore, not credible. It is just used as an element of literary style by intellectuals who have long ago become bourgeois. With profound gratitude, they turn to thinkers who open their hearts for the beauty of the world and humanity.

Teilhard certainly has a finer and more sensitive perception of the basic good preserved in creation than for the evil which sin has brought into it. But it is high time to throw a proper light on this aspect before the new generation, too, becomes benumbed by looking back upon burning Sodom. Supported by the divine promise, it is time for us to look forward as Lot did. "Flee for your life; do not look back or stop anywhere in the valley" (Gen. 19:17). This is expressed even more drastically in the second letter of Peter (2:22): "The dog turns back to his own vomit." This is the evangelical answer to the question of how to cope with the past.

The question arises now whether the new vision, given here by Teilhard, does not actually lead us beyond the basic area of Christian revelation. The question is whether, as a result of a Christian interpretation of evolution, a *new religion* has been developed which leaves the Christian revelation behind, as the Christian religion once overtook Judaism. Is this not a universalism with a greater Christ, as remote from the Jesus Christ of the old dogmas as the Omega, the "God more radiant than Jehovah," is from the biblical Jehovah and his "neolithic patriarchalism"?

At this point, I believe that the usual dogmatic charges raised against Teilhard are not as justified as it is claimed. He was criticized for having made the history of salvation a kind of extension and continuation of natural history, placing it thus under a law of determinism which, in the final analysis, leaves no room for guilt and grace which generate the significant tension of the history of salvation. This criticism is not warranted.

Teilhard has never tried to do what the nineteenth-century Darwinists of the Büchner-type did, namely, to transfer the natural laws of the animal kingdom to the human area and to human history. On the contrary, he emphasized tirelessly that the specific sign of the noosphere, into which man entered by acquiring self-consciousness, is freedom. Advancing into consciousness means to advance into the sphere of freedom. In this respect, Teilhard was not a follower of Hegel, but of Schelling. His theology flows into a theology of freedom. The charge that Teilhard converted prophecy into prognosis is therefore wrong and could be easily refuted by many of his statements.

Another equally unwarranted charge is that Teilhard overlooks the power of evil.[6] This is not true. Again the most recent publications of his works give a very unequivocal answer. There is one point we have to make, however: He actually suffered the same fate as Leibniz and any other thinker who looks at the totality of world-development and aims at a conspectus of philosophy of nature and philosophy of history. In the theological field, this means that he aims at a synopsis of natural theology and theology of the history of salvation. Evil, which includes moral evil, becomes a *malum metaphysicum*, an element of evolution, an artful trick, by which resistance and abuses of freedom and intelligence, lead life to broader expansion and even higher development. Thus it becomes a ruse of reason designed to bring about the

victory of the good. Teilhard again brings to light the
very old problem of theodicy which also dominated Leibniz. The only correct comparison with thinkers of the
past would therefore be with Leibniz rather than with
Thomas Aquinas or Aristotle. Leibniz turned away from
the Sodom and Gomorrah of the Thirty Years War. He
recognized the world which was still smoking from the
religious conflagrations and the pyres of the Inquisition
as the world of God, the "best of all possible worlds."

It appears to me that criticism has to start at another
point. Through the centuries, all creative effects of the
Christian message were determined by the original message: "Repent, for the Kingdom of God is near," or "Behold, I will come soon!" The great reforms and reformations of the Church happened under the sign of the
imminent return of the Lord and of the advent of the end
of time.

But under the sign of evolutionist thinking, the long-
term concept of time which characterizes evolution also
penetrates into the history of salvation. Reconstructing
history to the earliest period of human genesis, which is
a matter of millions of years, leads to an extension of the
periods of future evolution which is also extended to dimensions of aeons, of millions of years. This is the last
phase in the abandonment of the expectation of an early
advent of the Kingdom of God, a development which
started in the second century of the Christian era.

Under the influence of this stretching into periods of
aeons, the original spiritual and moral impulse of the
Christian expectation of the end of time fades out. The
idea that all lines of evolution converge in point Omega,
leads, without fail, to the idea of *Universal Redemption.*
Humanity thus absorbs the Church and final judgment
becomes identical with the selection process of evolution
in which much is sacrificed and eliminated. For its creator, this theology may still be filled with ethical impulses.

But its popularization cannot avoid a danger to which the supporters of universal redemption were exposed since the days of Origen: the dangerous feeling of security and the consciousness of being well taken care of in that stream of convergence which runs irresistibly toward its Omega.

This standpoint has another result: The existentialists have been mesmerized by the abysmal problems of our own existence and have developed microscopic methods of analysis to study the symptoms of decay in our culture. Teilhard, on the other hand, misleads us into looking at our own short-range problems through the wrong end of a telescope, as it were, from the viewpoint of future phases of evolution. The result is that all that moves us today shrinks into a passing and rather inconsequential episode. The real problems of our time are minimized to such an extent that they appear, in Teilhard's reversed telescope, only an optical distortion or not at all. Eschatological optimism threatens to shift to eschatological frivolity, and there are few among us who can afford that.

In this respect, I agree with the criticism of Adolf Portmann, who concluded his essay on Teilhard de Chardin in the 1959 issue of *Merkur* as follows: "The aim of evolution toward pole Omega is far beyond the range of sight of our lives. I fear that such a distant view will help little when we have to determine the immediate goals out of the human narrowness of our lives."[7]

As a result of the futuristic distance which he keeps from the pressing problems of our time, Teilhard sometimes shows an amazing lack of feeling and even inhumanity which can only be explained by the supreme, intellectual abstractness of his thinking. It is the coldness of feeling of a world-revolution commissar. A good illustration is his attitude to war and the atom bomb.

The letters which Teilhard de Chardin wrote during World War I to his cousin Marguerite Teillard are per-

haps the strangest contribution to this type of war literature, of which some has since become classical. Authors of
this kind of literature, whether they stood on the right or
left politically, usually agreed on one point: They all gave
strong emphasis to an indictment of war for its senselessness, brutality, atrocity, and irreparable devastation of
the human substance. In his war letters (incidentally, he
never thought that they would be published), Teilhard
deals with this point marginally or not at all. On the contrary: If his friends are deeply shaken by the experience
of the senselessness of war, he tries to convert them to a
positive interpretation of war as an honorable contribution toward natural evolution.[8]

From the distant viewpoint of evolution, war appears to
him as co-operation in the progress of nature, as active
assistance to "natural evolution." Even his participation
in the severe struggle for Verdun and in the horrible
barrage-fire cannot shatter his futuristic morality. All he
feels is "honor" to be present at a decisive point of revolutionary dynamics.[9] Indeed, as a priest, he regrets that
his priestly status condemns him to serve only as a medi-
cal orderly and deprives him of the right to jump over
the edge of the trench with bayonet or hand grenade to
participate in the real man-to-man fight.[10] He even
comes to the conclusion that he would be "more priestly"
as a member of the fighting force with a grenade in his
hand or behind a machine gun.[11]

His way of looking at the problems of our time through
the reversed telescope of futurism becomes even more
apparent in his opinion on the *atomic bomb*. The bomb-
ing of Hiroshima filled Teilhard with enthusiastic admiration for the scientific-technological progress which
this result of the teamwork of a scientific superbrain
meant for humanity and human consciousness.

It is significant that his observations do not refer to
Hiroshima but to the first test-explosion in Arizona and

the subsequent atomic tests at Bikini. As Robert Jungk reported in his book *Brighter Than a Thousand Suns,* atomic scientists who had remained in Germany prevented the development of a German atomic bomb in the service of Hitler.[12] Teilhard was not disturbed by inhibitions of this kind. "Isn't it the supreme duty of every man to push the creative forces of understanding and action to their extreme limits? And, incidentally, is there a power in the world capable of halting the progress of human thinking along any path which it has taken?"[13]

The dead and wounded of Hiroshima are for him unavoidable sacrifices on the road toward fulfilling the duty of pushing evolution forward. In the final analysis, the justification of such sacrifices is the fact that such superdimensional possibilities of destruction become a guarantee for peace. The following is his interpretation of the Bikini tests: "Despite their military setting, the recent explosions at Bikini therefore show a humanity which is at peace both internally and externally. They announce the coming of the spirit of the earth."[14] The possibility of a catastrophic result of this evolution he rejects with a smile. After all, on the entire planet there is the instinct of the self-preservation of life![15]

The consequences of Teilhard's futuristic method of observation are most pronounced in his judgment on the political and ideological tensions of our time. What agitates humanity today, namely, the confrontation between the communist bloc and the free democracies, appears exaggerated in Teilhard's futuristic view. He feels that men fail to realize the far-reaching inner identity of the various, already-existing forms of socialization which drive toward convergence.

Teilhard's eschatology combines an early and a remote expectation. The remote expectation is extended into unimaginable periods of time by the doctrine of evolution. There is an obvious tendency to subdue all fears of an eschatological nature. "We have a few million years ahead of us yet!" he exclaimed in Peking in 1941.[16] It is quite soothing that there is still such a long period ahead to complete the evolution of future humanity. But Teilhard states with great emphasis that the next forward jump in the evolution of humanity is imminent. It is prepared by the radical socialization and totalization of mankind which is under way now.

When Teilhard refers to the imminent forward jump to the next stage of evolution, his prognosis assumes a revolutionary character for two reasons: (1) he interprets Marxism in a very positive way as a neo-Humanism based on the idea of evolution and thus completely ignores the anti-Christian and anti-ecclesiastical religious policies in the countries of the Eastern bloc; (2) he represents collectivization and socialization as the inevitable and inescapable tendency of the present phase of evolution, thus from the outset paralyzing resistance against the totalitarian elements of evolution.

Rather monotonously, Teilhard repeats the thesis, in his essays and lectures on the future evolution of man, that a further collectivization of human society is unavoidable. Under the impact of modern science, technology and economy, society presses toward planetization. Thus in January 1947 he noted: "The earth would rather stop turning than humanity as a whole would stop organizing for unity."[17] In a similar vein, he wrote, in his 1949 essay "Does humanity move?":

> You can see with the naked eye that the earth is contracting. Hundreds of millions of people are living on its surface. They must meet the pressure to which they are subject and must adjust to it. This not only *forces* them to make technical accommodations with one another, but also to tolerate or bring into play the inexhaustible interpsychic binding forces which

originate in the revolutionary capacity of reflexion. The human molecules are pressed closely together. The more closely they are pressed to each other, *the less they can help from* becoming fused together, body and soul. The rise of the social principle, the rise of the machine, the rise of science . . . we talk rather naïvely and are surprised (sometimes even indignant), as if these various events and their coincidence were something fortuitous or unexpected. How can we overlook that, on the contrary, we are dealing here with three facets of one and the same completely regulated process of planetary scope?[18]

The result of these ideas is a re-evaluation of the forms of socialization and collectivization of humanity which were created by Marxism and communism. Teilhard criticizes the Western democracies frequently and with an irony that can hardly be ignored. But he seldom utters a negative judgment on Marxism and communism. Even in the rare instances, where this happens, there is always an apologetic or extenuating qualification. Seen in their totality, his works are dominated by a visibly growing tendency to justify Marxism.[19]

In his lecture to the World Congress of Faiths for Peace delivered in New York on March 8, 1947, he makes the following remarks on socialism:

Take the two extremes in your environment today: A Marxist here, and a Christian there. Both are convinced of their particular doctrine. We take for granted that both are also deeply animated by an equally strong faith in man. Is it not certain, is it not a fact of daily experience that the more strongly these two men believe in the future of the world, the more one feels that the other has this belief, the more one will have a deep sympathy for the other— from man to man? It is not a simple, sentimental sympathy, but a sympathy based on the mystical evidence that they travel together and that in one way or another, and despite all conflicting formulations, they will eventually find each other again on the same summit.

Each of them believes, undoubtedly in his own way and in divergent directions, that he has solved the ambiguity of the world, once and for all. But this divergence is really neither complete nor final. Driven to the end, the two roads will eventually come closer to each other. For, by its nature, each faith ascends. Whatever ascends, must inevitably converge.[20]

What Christianity and Marxism have in common, according to Teilhard, is their faith in progress, in the convergence of humanity. Here the religion of evolution appears as a super-religion, joining Christians and non-Christians. In a lecture, delivered in Peking in 1941, Teilhard says:

The new soul for a new world: a regenerated faith in human progress. Christians and non-Christians— all men who are animated by this particular conviction—form a homogeneous category. Although they are at the two outside wings of advancing humanity, they can march forward, hand in hand, without obliterating the boundary lines. Their attitudes are not mutually exclusive—in fact, one is virtually the extension of the other. They only demand to complement one another. Why are they waiting to recognize and love one another? The "Sacred Union" is the common front of all those who believe that the universe is still advancing and that it is our task to bring about its advance. Should this not be the active minority, the firm nucleus, around which the unanimity of tomorrow should develop?[21]

The "Sacred Union" between progressive Christianity and Marxism is the modern counterpart of the "Holy Alliance" which once joined the Christian monarchs of Europe, the Orthodox Emperor of Russia, the Roman Catholic Emperor of Austria, and the Protestant King of Prussia against Napoleon, the Antichrist from the West. The "Sacred Union" gives a clear indication, even by the choice of words, how much Teilhard's position is opposed to the traditional anti-modernism of the recent popes (Pius IX, X, XII) which prevailed until now.

For Teilhard, the religion of progress and evolution is not in itself the expression of a new man, the *homo progressivus* who will take the place of the old-fashioned, anti-modernist, and actually already obsolete, bourgeois man. *Homo progressivus* is the intermediate stage between *homo sapiens,* from whom we descend, and the superman of the distant future.

Faced by the advance of the victorious army of Mao Tse-tung, Teilhard says in Peking, in 1945[22]:

A total and possibly final split of humanity, not on the level of wealth but on the basis of their faith in progress—this is the great phenomenon which we are experiencing now . . . If we look at it in this manner, the old Marxist contrast between worker and exploiter becomes obsolete, or at least, we recognize it as a poorly drawn boundary line. In the final analysis, it is not a social class, but a spirit—the spirit of movement—which aims to split humanity into two camps. On this side are those, who consider the world that has to be built as a comfortable place to live in. On the other side, there are the others who can only visualize the world as a machine of progress or, better yet, as an organism in a state of progress. Here, in essence, the "spirit of the bourgeoisie," and there, the true "workers of the earth." Of the latter, you can easily predict that they will be the humanity of to-morrow. This will come about without violence or hatred, but just by the effect of the biological domi-nant. Here the refuse—in French, *le déchet* which means dregs, refuse, trash—there the generating forces and the elements of planetization.[23]

The bourgeoisie is thus relegated, a priori, to the ref-use heap.

Indeed, Teilhard foresees an early and inevitable frat-ernization with the co-religionists of the other camp. At Christmastime in 1945 he announces to his audience:

Recently, a new substance has turned up in the thinking "magma." It is a new element, not yet listed in any catalogue, but of greatest importance. It is the *homo progressivus,* as we might call him, that is, a man for whom the future of this earth counts more than its present. No racial, social or religious barrier seems to be impenetrable for this power of attraction to which I refer. I experienced it hundreds of times myself and everybody can repeat the same experi-ence. Whatever the country, the religious faith, or the social class of the person may be, to whom I ad-dress myself, if the same fire of expectation glows in both of us, there will immediately be a profound, final and total contact. It is unimportant that, on the basis of our education and training, we express our hopes in a different way. We feel that we belong to the same species. Thus we determine that we are even tied together by our contrasts, as if there were a certain vital dimension in which every effort brings us closer to each other—not only chest-to-chest but heart-to-heart.[24]

Those who belong to this new race of evolution, are already beyond the present tensions. In answer to a

UNESCO inquiry on the future of democracy, Teilhard declared in 1949:

> This strange and obstinate division within all democratic movements into the two opposing concepts of liberalism and planned economy (that is, individualism and totalitarianism) is actually not difficult to interpret. The explanation becomes self-evident if we state that these seemingly contradictory alternatives of the social ideal actually correspond to personalization and totalization, the two natural components, whose interplay is the biological determinant of the nature and progress of the genesis of man. On the one side, the element becomes the center, on the other side, the group. Sometimes one, sometimes the other of the two vectors is getting more emphasis and outweighs the other. This can reach such a degree that it wants to absorb it altogether. A step to the right, a step to the left . . . this does not involve any contradiction to a principle, just a disturbance of the equilibrium, a disharmony, or even (why not?) an unavoidable and necessary form of alternation. I repeat that, biologically, there is no real democracy without a carefully weighed amalgamation of the two supplementary factors which, in their pure form, are represented in individualistic regimes here and in authoritarian ones there.[25]

The last, possibly still remaining, resistance against this general biological trend of evolution is removed by Teilhard's argument that it would be useless anyway. The tendency of his biological determinism therefore becomes noticeable even in the field of political ideology.

Even more unequivocally, he stated in "The Idea of Democracy" in 1949: "What we have to expect, in the end, is a planetary co-ordination of the human mass and energy. It coincides with a maximum of emanations of the spirit, an external and internal *planetarisation* of humanity, at the same time. We will proceed in this direction inevitably, under the growing pressure of *social determinisms* . . . Why do we hesitate? Instead of putting up a futile resistance against the plasmatic powers of the planet which carries us, or surrender to them like serfs, why don't we allow that our lives be widened and suffused by the rising light of this second genesis of man?"[26]

This is the point at which he crosses the dangerous borderline, at which biological determinism is transposed into human history. In the name of an allegedly unavoidable totalization, intellectual and political positions are evacuated in advance. Our future, in coming generations, will depend upon our ability to hold these positions in attack and defense.

A borderline in Teilhard's interpretation of Christian love has been crossed here as well. He hopes that compression, the pressure of overpopulation, the technological development of world traffic and the world economy, can be converted into a socialization of adhesion which is dominated by the spontaneous mutual love of the various social molecules. Instead of outside pressure, inner attraction should shape the form of planetarized humanity.

But, at a decisive point, his evolutionist idea of *amorisation* of the human molecules does not reach the scope of the concept of love in the Gospel. In "Thoughts on Progress," a lecture delivered in the French Embassy of Peking on March 3, 1941, Teilhard stated: "Love one another by recognizing the genesis of the same God in the depth of each other's being. This sentence, which was spoken, for the first time, two thousand years ago, has the aim to become nowadays the essential structural law of what we are calling progress and evolution."[27]

Teilhard is so much in love with his theology of evolution that he bases it on a quotation from Holy Scripture which does not exist in the Holy Scriptures at all. The sentence "Love one another by recognizing the genesis of the same God in the depth of each other's being" is not from the New Testament. It was invented on March 3, 1941 at the French Embassy in Peking. The sentence in the New Testament is: "You shall love the Lord your God, and your neighbor as yourself." Here love does not depend upon the recognition of the genesis of God in your neighbor. It is directed immediately to the neighbor himself, as a person, with all the singleness and uniqueness of his actions and his suffering, his imperfection and his virtue, his misery and his greatness. The danger to which the love of the God of evolution is exposed is that, through it, the love of man, the love of the neighbor, of the "thou" will be lost. The neighbor, the fellow-human, will submerge in the "human dough," in the "magma of evolution." In the *amorisation* of evolution, *love* will be *extinguished*.

In view of the strange ambivalence of Teilhard's concept of the future of man, it is important that we are not misled, by the ardor of hope, to minimize our present situation and to make love a mere function. Two great thinkers of the eighteenth century have expressed this in an unsurpassed way. What they say is even more valid today—in view of Teilhard's theological interpretation of evolution—than it was then, at the time of the first attempt to understand evolution as part of the history of salvation:

Herder: Brethren, let us work right under the cloud, with a courageous and joyous heart. For we are working for a great future.[28]

Pascal: It is dangerous to show man too clearly, how much he resembles the animal, unless we show him his greatness, at the same time. But it is also dangerous to show him his greatness, without showing him his baseness. The greatest danger is to leave him in ignorance about one and the other. However, it is most useful to show him both. Man should not believe that he is like an animal, and he should not believe either that he is like an angel. But he should not remain ignorant about one and the other. He must rather know both.

Man is not an angel, and not an animal. It is a misfortune that whoever plays the part of an angel will become an animal.[29]

NOTES

INTRODUCTION

1 Ernst Benz, "Das Bild des Übermenschen bei Leopold Ziegler," *Der Übermensch*. Zurich/Stuttgart, 1948, pp. 375 ff.

2 Paul Schütz, particularly in *Parusia, Hoffnung und Prophetie*. Heidelberg, 1960.

3 See chapters XII and XIII.

I

1 Literature for early Christian eschatology:

Heinz-Dietrich Wendland, *Die Eschatologie des Reiches Gottes bei Jesus*. Gütersloh, 1931.

――――, *Geschichtsanschauung und Geschichtsbewusstsein im Neuen Testament*. Göttingen, 1938.

Rudolf Otto, *The Kingdom of God and the Son of Man*. Boston: Starr King, 1957.

Werner Georg Kümmel, *Promise and Fulfilment*. Naperville, Ill.: Alec R. Allenson, 1957.

Oscar Cullmann, *Christ and Time*. Philadelphia: Westminster, 1964.

Hans Bietenhard, *Das Tausendjährige Reich*. Zurich: 1945, 2d ed. 1955.

Paul Althaus, *Die letzten Dinge*. Gütersloh: 1922, 6th ed. 1956.

Georges Florovsky, *Eschatology in the Patristic Age. An Intro-duction* (Studia Patristica II, Texte und Untersuchungen, Book v, Vol. 64, pp. 235–54). Berlin, 1957.

Karl Heim, *The World: Its Creation and Consummation*. Philadelphia: Fortress, 1962.

2 Hermann Gunkel, *Schöpfung und Chaos in Urzeit und Endzeit*. Göttingen: 1895, 2d ed. 1921.

Paul Volz, *Die Eschatologie der jüdischen Gemeinde*. Tübingen, 2d ed. 1934.

Hugo Gressmann, *Ursprung der israelitisch-jüdischen Eschatologie*. Göttingen, 1905.

Gustav Hoelscher, *Die Ursprünge der jüdischen Eschatologie*. Giessen, 1925.

Sigmund Mowinckel, *He That Cometh. The Messianic Concept in the Old Testament and Later Judaism*. Nashville: Abingdon, 1956.

3 Entry into Jerusalem: Mt. 21:1–9; Mk. 11:1–10; Jn. 12:12–16.

4 On the Trial of Jesus: John Knox, *The Death of Christ; The Cross in New Testament History and Faith*. Nashville: Abingdon, 1958.

5 Rudolf Otto, *Reich Gottes und Menschensohn*, pp. 141 f., 160 f.

6 Friedrich Noetscher, *Altorientalischer und Alttestamentlicher Auferstehungsglaube*. Würzburg, 1926.

Hugo Gressmann, *Der Messias*. Göttingen, 1929.

Paul Volz, *Die Eschatologie der jüdischen Gemeinde*. Tübingen, 2d ed. 1934.

Kurt Schubert, *Die Religion des nachbiblischen Judentums*. Freiburg, 1955.

7 On Duplication of eschatology:

Hans Conzelmann, *Die Mitte der Zeit*. Tübingen: 1954, 4th ed. 1962.

Friedrich Guntermann, *Die Eschatologie des Hl. Paulus*. Münster, 1932.

Christian Walther, *Typen des Reich-Gottes-Verständnisses*. Munich, 1961.

Walter Nigg, *Das ewige Reich*. Erlenbach/Zurich, 1944.

8 Edgar Hennecke, *Neutestamentliche Apokryphen* (2d ed. 1924), XXXVIII. 12, according to Irenaeus V. 33:3 f., p. 545. (U.S. ed.: *New Testament Apocrypha*; Vol. 1, Gospels and Related Writings. Philadelphia: Westminster, 1963.)

9 Didache 10:6 (Hennecke, *ibid.*, XXXIX. 10, p. 564).

10 Tertullian, *De carnis resurrectione* c. 22 (CSEL XLVII, p. 54); see also *De oratione* c. 5.

11 Didymus of Alexandria, *De trinitate* III. 4:1 (PG 39,984).

12 Epiphanius, *Panarion* 48. 4 (GCS II, p. 233).

13 E. Hennecke, "Vom Übermenschen," *Christliche Welt* 47 (1924), 748.

II

1 Albert Schweitzer, *Geschichte der Leben-Jesu-Forschung* (Tübingen, 5th ed. 1933), p. 634.
2 Albert Schweitzer, *Die Mystik des Apostels Paulus* (Tübingen, 1930), chap. v, pp. 80 f. *Ibid.*, chap. XIII, pp. 324 f., 341 f.
3 *Ibid.*, p. 341.
4 Adolf von Harnack, *Dogmengeschichte* (Freiburg, 2d ed., 1888), p. 18. (Available in English: *History of Dogma*, 18 vols., Gloucester, Mass., 1962.)
5 Martin Werner, *Die Entstehung des christlichen Dogmas.* Bern-Leipzig, 1941. (*Formation of Christian Dogma: A Presentation of the History of the Problem.* Boston: Beacon, 1965.)
6 *Ibid.*, p. 133.
7 *Ibid.*, p. 669.
8 Origen, *Matt. comm. series* 50 on Mt. 24:30 (GCS XI, p. 312; Leipzig, 1933).
9 On Augustine, see Ernst Benz, *Augustins Lehre von der Kirche*, on the occasion of Augustine's 1600th birthday, November 13, 1954. (Abhandlungen der Akademie der Wissenschaft und der Literatur, Mainz, 1954.)
10 Cyprian, *Ep.* 73 *ad Jubaianum* 21 (CSEL III.2, p. 795).
11 Augustine, *Sermo* 267. 4, 4 (PL 38, 1231).
12 Augustine, *Epist.* 185. 11, 50 (CSEL LVII.43).
13 Augustine, *Sermo ad Caesareensis ecclesiae plebem* 6 (CSEL LIII.167).
14 Augustine, *Contra Secundinum Manichaeum* 26 (CSEL LII.1).
15 Augustine, *Contra Cresconium grammaticum* 3. 51, 57 (CSEL LII.463).
16 Augustine transferred the term "character" from military usage to priestly ordination.
17 Augustine, *In evangelium Johannis* 30. 1 (PL 35, 1632).
18 Augustine, *De baptismo* 1. 7, 9 (CSEL LI.145). *De unitate ecclesiae* 3. 6 (CSEL LII).
19 Augustine, *Enarrationes in Psalmos* 44. 32 (PL 36, 513).
20 Augustine, *Sermo* 227 (PL 38, 1100).
21 Augustine, *Contra litteras Petiliani* 2. 51, 118 (CSEL LII.3, p. 88).

III

1 Ernst Benz, *Ecclesia Spiritualis: Kirchenidee und Geschichtstheologie der franziskanischen Reformation.* Stuttgart, 1934; Darmstadt, 1964 (reprint).

Ernst Benz, "Creator Spiritus. Die Geistlehre des Joachim von Fiore." *Eranos-Jahrbuch* XXV (1957), 285–355.

2 Herbert Grundmann, *Neue Forschungen über Joachim von Fiore.* Marburg, 1950. Also his "Kleine Beiträge über Joachim von Fiore," *Zeitschrift für Kirchengeschichte* XLVIII, N.F. XI, 137 ff.

E. Russo, *Bibliografia Gioachimitica.* Rome, 1954.

3 As in the case of the Hussites. But Matthias von Janow (died 1394) shows the same tendencies and so does, through him, his disciple Jakob von Mies (Jakoubek-Jacobellus), a friend of Huss and "second founder of Hussitism."

4 *Concordia Novi ac Veteris Testamenti* (Venice, 1519), lib. V, c. 84, fol. 112; see Ernesto Buonaiuti, *Gioacchino da Fiore,* p. 135; *Expositio in Apocalypsim* (Venice, 1527), fol. 82c; *Protokoll von Anagni,* pp. 131–32.

5 See "Tractatus Super Quatuor Evangelia," published by Ernesto Buonaiuti in *Fonti per la Storia d'Italia, Scrittori sec. XII* (Rome, 1930), pp. 111, 7 ff.

6 Tractatus, pp. 154, 26 ff.

7 Tractatus, p. 31, 5: *"proficere in genus electum et regnum spirituale."*

8 Ernst Benz, "Creator Spiritus," *Eranos-Jahrbuch* XXV, 317.

9 Tractatus, pp. 117, 25 f. See I Cor. 2:13 and Jn. 16:13.

10 *Concordia,* lib. II, tract. 1, c. 1.

11 *Concordia,* lib. III, c. 9.

12 On the movement of the Friends of God, see Rufus M. Jones, *The Flowering of Mysticism. The Friends of God in the Fourteenth Century.* New York: Macmillan, 1939.

13 *Expositio in Apocalypsim,* c. 1 at verse 7, c. III: *"Transibit labor doctrinae et remanebit diligendi libertas."*

14 Thus in Tractatus, pp. 292, 14 ff.

15 *Concordia,* lib. II, tract. 1, c. 28; lib. I, fol. 22 b-c; Tractatus, p. 24 n. 1, and p. 281 n. 1.

16 On the manifold aftereffects of Joachimitism, particularly its doctrine of the third "status" of the Holy Ghost, in the area of Bohemian Hussitism and its penetration into Central Germany in the second half of the fifteenth century, see Ruth Kestenberg-Gladstein, "The 'Third Reich.' A Fifteenth-century Polemic against Joachism and Its Background," *Journal of the Warburg and Courtauld Institutes* XVIII, 3–4, 245–95.

17 Tractatus, 43, 3 ff.

IV

1 Eugen Rosenstock-Huessy, *Die europäischen Revolutionen und der Charakter der Nationen.* Stuttgart/Koln, 1951.

2 Karl Griewank, *Der neuzeitliche Revolutionsbegriff: Entstehung und Entwicklung* (Weimar, 1955), chap. XI. On Hegel, see pp. 260 ff; Karl Marx, pp. 270 ff.

3 *Thomas Müntzer: Sein Leben und seine Schriften.* Published with an introduction by Otto H. Brandt (Jena, 1933).

4 Walter Nigg, *Heimliche Weisheit.* Zurich/Stuttgart, 1959. See chapter on Thomas Münzer: pp. 43 ff.

5 Concerning the *Deus nudus,* see Meister Eckhart, *Lateinische Werke. Sermo* XI, No. 115, p. 108; *Sermo* IX, No. 99, p. 94; *Sermo* XI.2, No. 120, pp. 114 f.; *Sermo* XXIV.2, No. 246, p. 225, and No. 249, p. 227.

6 See Meister Eckhart, *Works.* Translated by C. Evans (Naperville, Ill.: Allenson, n.d.), Sermons 11 and 7.

7 The most revealing study on the Brethren of the Free Spirit and their revolutionary elements can be found in Norman Cohn, *The Pursuit of the Millennium* (New York: Oxford, 1957). Chapters VII and VIII: "An Elite of Amoral Supermen," pp. 149–85.

8 George Huntston Williams, *The Radical Reformation.* Philadelphia: Westminster, 1962.

9 Karl Kautsky, *Vorläufer des modernen Sozialismus* (2 vols.; Stuttgart, 1920). Before him, Friedrich Engels had already referred to Münzer in *The Peasant War in Germany.* New York: International Publications Service, 1926. For the latest Soviet-Russian presentation of Münzer, see M. M. Smirin, *Die Volksreformation des Thomas Müntzer und der grosse Bauernkrieg.* Berlin, 1952.

10 Ernst Bloch, *Thomas Müntzer als Theologe der Revolution* 1921, p. 23; and Otto H. Brandt, p. 5.

11 *Vorrede ins Buch dieser Lobgesänge* Otto H. Brandt, p. 113.

12 *Müntzer: Leben und Schriften,* p. 61.

13 *Ibid.,* p. 67.

14 On the feudalization of the Church, see Alois Schulte, *Der Adel und die deutsche Kirche im Mittelalter* (2d ed. 1922; Studien zur Sozial-, Rechts- und Kirchengeschichte). Darmstadt, 1958 (reprint).

15 Ernst Benz, "Über den Adel in der deutschen Mystik," *Deutsche Vierteljahrsschriften für Literaturwissenschaft und Geistesgeschichte* XIV, 4 (1936), pp. 505–35.

16 Angelus Silesius, *Cherubinischer Wandersmann,* Book 4, No. 227. (Collected poetic works published by H. L. Held, vol. 3[2d ed. 1924], p. 174.)

17 *Ibid.*, Book 6, No. 232: vol. 3, p. 270.
18 O. H. Brandt, pp. 20 ff.; Documents, pp. 83 ff.
19 *Müntzer: Leben und Schriften*, pp. 62, 66.
20 More frequently, the Latin text, as in the conclusion of the letter to Zeyss, the tax-collector; *ibid.*, p. 70.
21 *Ibid.*, pp. 75 f.
22 *Ibid.*, p. 76.
23 *Ibid.*, p. 78.
24 On the revolutionary aspect of Messianism in Europe, see Jakob Taubes, *Abendländische Eschatologie* (Bern, 1947), pp. 106 ff. on Münzer; J. L. Talmon, *Political Messianism* (London: Secker and Warburg, 1960); for Asia, see Sarkisyanz, *Russland und der Messianismus des Ostens* (Tübingen, 1958).

V

1 Concerning Herder's idea of revolution, see Karl Griewank, *op. cit.*, pp. 22 ff.; Herder, *Werke.* Vol XVIII (1793), p. 332.
2 Immanuel Kant, *Der Streit der Fakultäten;* in Complete Works (Leipzig, 1912), vol. I, 2d section 6, pp. 637 ff.
3 *Ibid.*, p. 646.
4 Franz von Baader, *Über den Evolutionismus und Revolutionismus, oder positive und negative Evolution des Lebens überhaupt und des sozialen Lebens insbesondere;* Complete Works, vol. 6.
5 Franz von Baader, *Revision der Philosopheme der Hegelschen Schule;* Complete Works, vol. 9, p. 353.
6 Franz von Baader, *Vorlesungen über eine künftige Theorie des Opfers* (Münster, 1836), p. 25.
7 *Ibid.*, p. 21.
8 The Christian roots of the idea of evolution were pointed out in particular by Kurt Breysig in his work *Gestaltungen des Entwicklungsgedankens.* Berlin, 1940. See also: Heinrich Schmidt, *Geschichte der Entwicklungslehre.* Leipzig, 1918.
9 B. H. Brockes, *Physikalische und moralische Gedanken über die drey Reiche der Natur. Nebst seinen übrigen nachgelassenen Gedichten, als des irdischen Vergnügens in Gott Neunter und letzter Theil* (Hamburg, 1748), p. 282.
10 Francis Darwin, ed., *Charles Darwin: His Life* (New York, 1893), p. 65. Also in Nora Barlow, *The Autobiography of Charles Darwin, 1809–1882* (London, 1958), p. 92.
11 Charles Darwin, *The Descent of Man* (London, 1891), pp. 440 f. Darwin's optimistic interpretation of evolution is also expressed at the end of his *Origin of Species:* "As all the living forms of life are the lineal descendants of those which lived long before the Silurian epoch, we may feel certain

that the ordinary succession by generation has never once been broken, and that no cataclysm has desolated the whole world. Hence we may look with some confidence to a secure future of great length. And as natural selection works solely by and for the good of each being, all corporeal and mental endowments will tend to progress towards perfection."

12 Francis Darwin, *Charles Darwin: His Life* (1893), p. 68—letter of July 3, 1881.

13 *Ibid.*, chap. 3, p. 66; and Nora Barlow, *op. cit.*, pp. 92 f.

14 J. B. Bury, *The Idea of Progress, An Inquiry into its Origin and Growth*, New York: Peter Smith, 1960 (first published in London, 1920: pp. 335 f., 345 f.): "Evolution itself . . . is a neutral scientific conception, compatible either with optimism or with pessimism. According to different estimates, it may appear to be a cruel sentence or a guarantee of steady amelioration. And it has been actually interpreted in both ways. . . . Evolution lends itself to a pessimistic as well as to an optimistic interpretation. The question whether it leads in a desirable direction or not is answered according to the temperament or the inquirer. In an age of prosperity and self-complacency, the affirmative answer was readily received, and the term evolution attracted to itself in common speech the implications of value which belong to Progress . . . When Mr. Frederic Harrison delivered in 1889 at Manchester an eloquent discourse on the 'New Era,' in which the dominant note was 'the faith in human progress in lieu of celestial rewards of the separate soul,' his general argument could appeal to immensely wider circles than the Positivists whom he was specially addressing."

15 David Friedrich Strauss, *Der alte und der neue Glaube*. Pt. III, chap. 62 (popular edition, n.d.), p. 56. (This work is available in English: *The Old Faith and the New* [New York: Holt, 1873].)

16 J. B. Bury, *op. cit.*, p. 342: "Many thoughtful and many thoughtless people were ready to discern—as Huxley suggested—in man's 'long progress through the past' a reasonable ground of faith in his attainment of a nobler future."

17 See Ernst Benz, *Eranos-Jahrbuch* XXVIII (1959), pp. 154 f.

18 Ludwig Büchner, *Sechs Vorlesungen über die Darwin'sche Theorie* (Leipzig, 1868), p. 253.

19 Alfred Russel Wallace, "The Origin of Human Races and the Antiquity of Man Deduced from the Theory of 'Natural Selection,'" *Journal of the Anthropological Society of London* II (1864), clxix–clxx.

20 Ludwig Büchner, *op. cit.*, p. 256.

21 *Ibid.*, p. 245.

22 Other works of Wallace which deserve to be mentioned in this connection: *The Wonderful Century* (1898, 2d ed. 1903);

Man's Place in the Universe (1903); *Autobiography* (*My Life*) (1905, 2d ed. 1908).

About him: J. Marchant, *A. R. Wallace: Letters and Reminiscenses* (2 vols., 1916); L. T. Hogben, *A. R. Wallace* (1918); B. Petronijevic, *Ch. Darwin and A. R. Wallace* (1925). See also Darwin-Wallace, *Documents Serving as Evidence for the Theory of Descent, over the Last Hundred Years, 1858/59–1958/59.*

23 First published in the *Anthropological Review* (May 1864).

24 Carl Du Prel, *Seherin von Prevorst* (Leipzig, n.d.), p. 12.

25 Lafcadio Hearn, *Kokoro* (Frankfurt a M, 1923), pp. 219 f.

26 Julian Huxley, *Evolution in Action* (New York, 1957), p. 157. Julian Huxley has presented his evolutionary Humanism in his collection *The Humanist Frame*, New York: Harper, 1962.

27 *Evolution in Action*, p. 127.

28 *Ibid.*, p. 126.

29 *Ibid.*, p. 131.

30 *Ibid.*, p. 134. On the development of parapsychic capacities, *ibid.*, p. 131: "The experiences of the mystics of all creeds and of the practitioners of Yoga prove what transcendent states of inner peace and unity of spirit the human personality is capable of."

31 See H. G. Wells, *The Future in America*, p. 32. E. E. Saltus (1855–1921) has written a number of books about utopia, such as: *The Lords of the Ghostland; A History of their Ideal* (1907); and (published posthumously) *The Uplands of Dream* (1925).

VI

1 Karl Marx-Friedrich Engels, *Briefwechsel*. Vol. II (1854–60), p. 547 (Engels to Marx, Dec. 12, 1859).

2 *Ibid.*, p. 548.

3 *Ibid.*, pt. II, p. 648. (Marx to Engels, Dec. 19, 1860—letter 720).

4 Karl Marx, *Auswahl*, edited by Franz Borkenau (Bücher des Wissens: Fischer-Bücherei, 1956), p. 200.

5 In *Festschrift Th. H. Masaryk zum 80. Geburtstage*, Pt. I (Bonn, 1930), pp. 265 ff.

6 Reprinted in *Sozialistische Aufsätze* (Berlin, 1921), p. 193.

7 Moses Hess, *Deutsches Bürgerbuch* (1845), pp. 38 ff.

8 Ernst Dronke (Berlin, Frankfurt a M, 1846), vol. II, pp. 115 f.

9 In *Sozialistiche Aufsätze*, p. 193.

10 Karl Marx-Friedrich Engels, *Gesammelte Schriften* (Stuttgart, 1902), vol. I, pp. 484 f.

11 D. F. Strauss, *Ein Nachwort als Vorwort*, completed on the last

day of the year 1877 (*Der alte und der neue Glaube*, p. 116).

12 Eugen Dühring, *Der Werth des Lebens* (published first in 1865; passage quoted from the 3d ed. 1881), p. 194.

13 *Ibid.*, p. 195.

14 *Ibid.*, p. 211.

15 *Ibid.*, p. 212.

16 Eugen Dühring, *Der Ersatz der Religion durch Vollkommeneres und die Abstreifung des Asiatismus* (Berlin-Nowawes, 1882), p. 16.

17 Eugen Dühring, *Der Werth des Lebens*, p. 139.

18 Rudolf Virchow, *Die Freiheit der Wissenschaft im modernen Staate*. Address delivered on September 22, 1878 at the Fiftieth Assembly of German Natural Scientists and Physicians in Munich.

19 Ernst Haeckel, "Deszendenztheorie und Sozialdemokratie," *Freie Wissenschaft und freie Lehre* (1878), chap. vi: p. 269 (Gemeinverständliche Werke, vol. V [Leipzig-Berlin, 1924]).

20 Ludwig Woltmann, *System des moralischen Bewusstseins mit besonderer Darlegung der Verhältnisse der kritischen Philosophie zu Darwinismus und Sozialismus* (Düsseldorf, 1898), p. 319.

21 *Ibid.*, p. 326.

22 Richard H. Grützmacher, *Modern-positive Vortrage* (Leipzig, 1904), pp. 45 ff.

23 *Ibid.*, p. 47.

24 *Ibid.*, p. 50.

25 *Ibid.*, p. 51, with reference to a publication of the former Dutch Prime Minister Kuyper, see Note 26.

26 Max Reischle *Zeitschrift für Theologie und Kirche* 12 (1912), 32, 36.

27 Ernst Haeckel, *Über unsere gegenwärtige Erkenntnis vom Ursprung des Menschen* (1899) (Gemeinverständliche Werke, vol. v, p. 374).

28 The Latin text: *evolutionis systema ut aiunt systema . . . qua quidem opinatione fautores communismi libenter fruunter ut suum materialismum dialecticum efficacius propugnent et evahant, omni notione theistica ex animis avulsa.*

29 The Anti-Modernist Oath was prescribed by Pope Pius X (*Motu proprio Sacrorum antistitum*, Sept. 1, 1910), on a preliminary basis, for the entire Roman Catholic clergy. It had the form of a profession of faith and represented a résumé and rejection of the errors of modernism, described in the encyclicals *Pascendi* and *Lamentabili*. At first, all priests who held ministerial or teaching positions were obliged to take the oath. Later on, it had to be sworn to orally and in writing by clerics before receiving the higher ordination; by

teachers of theology before assuming their office; by priests, church dignitaries, and superiors before their canonical installation. The order is in force to this day.

VII

References not further identified are to the Kröner edition of Nietzsche's works.

1 Vol. 77, p. 338.
2 Ernst Benz, "Das Bild des Übermenschen in der europäischen Geistesgeschichte," *Der Übermensch*, pp. 115 ff.
3 Vol. 76 (1887), p. 281, par. 16.
4 *Unschuld des Werdens* (Posthumous Works II, vol. 83, p. 258, par. 782).
5 *Die Geburt der Tragödie*, vol. 70, p. 198—in the Preface to Richard Wagner.
6 Introduction to *Zarathustra*, vol. 75, p. 8, par. 3.
7 Vol. 77, p. 195, par. 7.
8 Vol. 70, p. 251, par. 8.
9 Vol. 78, p. 462, par. 685.
10 *Ibid.*, p. 463, par. 685.
11 *Ibid.*, p. 459 f., par. 684.
12 Vol. 74, p. 248, par. 14.
13 Vol. 77, p. 140, par. 349.
14 Vol. 78, p. 286, par. 422.
15 Vol. 75, p. 8, par. 3.
16 *Ibid.*, p. 9, par. 3.
17 *Ibid.*, p. 17, par. 7.
18 *Ibid.*, p. 70.
19 *Ibid.*, p. 318, par. 3.
20 Vol. 78, p. 658, par. 1001.
21 On Zarathustra: *Unschuld des Werdens*, II, vol. 83, p. 446: 1214.
22 See p. 217.
23 Vol. 75, par. 84, par. 3.
24 *Ibid.*, p. 158.

VIII

1 Bibliography for the philosophy and history of technology:
Caspary, *Die Maschinenutopie*. Berlin, 1927.
Coudenhove-Kalergi, *Revolution durch Technik*. Vienna, 1932.
Reinhard Demoll, *Im Schatten der Technik, Beiträge zur Situation des Menschen in der modernen Zeit*. Munich, 1960.
Friedrich Dessauer, *Philosophie der Technik*. Bonn, 2d ed. 1928.
Eugen Diesel, *Das Phänomen der Technik, Zeugnisse, Deutung und Wirklichkeit*. Leipzig and Berlin, 1939.

G. Eichelberg, *Technik und Verantwortung*, 1932.

V. Engelhardt, *Weltanschauung und Technik*. Leipzig, 1922.

A. Faut, *Technik, technisches Zeitalter und Religion*, 1931.

H. Hardensett, *Philosophie der Technik*. Berlin, 1934.

Friedrich Georg Jünger, *Die Perfektion der Technik*. Frankfurt a M, 1946.

Ernst Kapp, *Grundlinien einer Philosophie der Technik, Zur Entstehungsgeschichte der Cultur aus neuen Gesichtspunkten*. Brunswick, 1877.

Hermann Keyserling, *Die neu entstehende Welt*. Darmstadt, 1926.

Paul Krannhals, *Der Weltsinn der Technik*. Munich, 1932.

Carl von Klinckowstroem, *Knaurs Geschichte der Technik*. Munich-Zurich, 1959.

Hanns Lilje, *Das technische Zeitalter*. Berlin, 2d ed. 1928.

Friedrich Muckermann, *Der Mensch im Zeitalter der Technik*. Lucerne, 1945.

Wayne W. Parrish, *Outline of Technocracy*. New York: Farrar, 1933.

Manfred Schröter, "Philosophie der Technik," *Handbuch der Philosophie*, vol. IV, 5 (Munich-Berlin, 1934).

Georg Siebers, *Das Ende des technischen Zeitalters*. Freiburg-Munich, 1963.

Robert Weyrauch, *Die Technik, ihr Wesen und ihre Beziehungen zu anderen Lebensgebieten*. Berlin, 1922.

Leopold Ziegler, *Zwischen Mensch und Wirtschaft*. Darmstadt, 1927.

Eberhard Zschimmer, *Philosophie der Technik*. 2d ed.; Jena, 1919.

2 A. P. Usher, *A History of Mechanical Inventions*. Boston: Beacon, 1959.

C. H. Singer and E. J. Homyard, *History of Technology*. 5 vols. New York: Oxford, 1954–58.

3 The image of God as a watchmaker is already known to Nominalist theology. Nicolaus von Oresme (died 1382) says in his commentary on Aristotle's *De caelo et mundo* that God set the world into motion as man starts a watch—he winds it up and then lets it run so that it will move on its own.

4 Hanns Lilje, *Das technische Zeitalter*, p. 76.

Paul Tillich, "Logos und Mythos der Technik." Address delivered on the occasion of the celebration of the 99th anniversary of the establishment of the Technische Hochschule, Dresden. Published in *Logos* XVI (1927), p. 364.

Friedrich Muckermann, *Der Mensch im Zeitalter der Technik*, p. 20.

5 See Maurice de Gandillac, "Place et signification de la technique dans le monde médiéval," *Technica e Casistica, a cura di Enrico Castelli*. Rome: Istituto di Studi Filosofici, 1964.

6 Hugo of St. Victor, *Eruditionis didascalicae libri septum*, lib. I, c. VIII (PL 176, 146).

7 The point of departure for the medieval theology of technology is Augustine's *De civitate Dei*, lib. XXII, c. XXIV.

8 Hanns Lilje, *Das technische Zeitalter*, p. 71.

9 On the connection between Pietism and social revolution, see Karl Kupisch, *Pietismus und Kommunismus*. Berlin, 1953. By the same author: *Das Jahrhundert des Sozialismus und die Kirche*. Berlin, 1958.

10 William Temple, "The Case for Evangelization," in *Proceedings of the Jerusalem Meeting of the International Missionary Council*, vol. I (1928), p. 380.

11 André Varagnac, "Das Altpaläolithicum," *Der Mensch der Urzeit, 600 000 Jahre Menschheitsgeschichte*, ed. by André Varagnac, chap. 2, p. 52.

12 Teilhard de Chardin in his essays which were collected by the editors in vol. 7 of *L'Activation de l'énergie*. On page 322, he states: *"La progressive et irrésistible unification technico-culturelle présentement en cours dans l'Humanité est un évènement de nature proprement organique, où le processus général de la biogénèse cosmique, non seulement demeure lisible, mais atteint dans le champ de notre expérience, un degré suprême de son développement."* In the same volume, Teilhard tries, in his article "Place de la Technique dans une biologie générale de l'Humanité," p. 161, to show *"que le progrès de l'industrie n'est pas accidentel, mais constitue un évènement susceptible d'entraîner les plus grandes conséquences spirituelles."* Then he states further on p. 164: *"L'homme est un être caractérisé par des mains et un cerveau: c'est un cérébro-manuel. Est-ce que nous ne pouvons pas reconnaître dans l'humanité globale ce caractère de cérébralité et de manualité? Les mains, c'est le machinisme; les machines sont trouvées par l'individu; l'outil est passé de l'individu au groupe. Alors apparaît cette entité de machinisme dont les développements sont tellement solidaires que morale et machine ne peuvent progresser l'une sans l'autre."*

The conclusions of his observations of January 16, 1947, are as follows (p. 167):

"Dans ces conclusions se trouve vérifiée jusqu'au bout la relation entre technique et conscience, la technique se présentant de telle façon qu'elle nous fait accéder à des pouvoirs d'un ordre plus grand, d'un ordre spirituel—et nous oblige à prendre position sur une religion."

13 L. Mumford, *The Story of Utopias*. London, 1923.

14 P. Ludz, "Utopie und Utopisten," *Religion in Geschichte und Gegenwart*, 3d ed., vol. VI, col. 1218.

15 Ernst Bloch, *Das Prinzip Hoffnung* (Frankfurt, 1959), p. 601—on Saint-Simon.

16 David Friedrich Strauss, *Der alte und der neue Glaube*, chap. 75, p. 69 (in American edition, chap. 71, p. 58).

17 From the *Stuttgarter Morgenblatt* of December 7, 1835.

18 Oswald Spengler, *Der Mensch und die Technik* (Munich, 1931), p. 87 (American edition: *Man and Technics: A Contribution to the Philosophy of Life.* New York: Knopf, 1932): "For the colored people, however—the Russians are always included in this category—Faustian technology is no inner necessity. Only Faustian man thinks, feels, and lives according to its pattern. It is a necessity for his *soul*. He does not need its economic results, but its *victories: navigare necesse est, vivere non est necesse*. For the "colored it is only a weapon in the fight against Faustian civilization. It is a weapon like a branch from a tree in the forest which you throw away when it has served its purpose . . . This technology of the machine will end with Faustian man and will, one day, be destroyed and *forgotten* . . . The history of this technology quickly approaches its inevitable end. It will be worn out from the inside, as all great forms of any culture. When and how this will happen, we do not know."

19 Georg Siebers, *Das Ende des technischen Zeitalters* (Freiburg-Munich, 1963), p. 28.

20 *Ibid.*, p. 31.

21 Eberhard Zschimmer deals with this in his *Philosophie der Technik. Vom Sinn der Technik und Kritik des Unsinns über die Technik* (Jena: Eugen Diederichs, 1914), p. 154.
   See also Paul Tillich: "Logos und Mythos der Technik." *Logos* XVI (1927), pp. 356 ff.

22 See the works of Eduard Justi, *Jahrbuch der Akademie der Wissenschaften und der Literatur* (Mainz, 1955), pp. 205 ff; (1957), pp. 207 ff; (1958), pp. 247 ff; and the international literature quoted there.

IX

1 Teilhard de Chardin had been unaware of the endeavors of Anglo-Saxon theology to deal with the doctrine of evolution and of the efforts of Anglo-Saxon natural scientists to develop the theory of evolution further on a theological level. In this respect, he fell victim to an unfavorable generalized judgment on Anglo-Saxon learning: "These Anglo-Saxons show themselves as notably learned, but embedded in their scientism, positivism, empiricism, neo-Darwinism: with few exceptions they are incapable of following philo-

sophical thought" (quoted from C. Cuénot, *Teilhard de Chardin* [Paris: Plon, 1958], p. 198).

Some important references to the theological interpretation of Darwinism in the United States can be found in Richard Hofstadter, *Social Darwinism in American Thought, 1860–1915* (The American Historical Association; Philadelphia: University of Pennsylvania Press, 1944).

2 On M. J. Savage, see *Dictionary of American Biography*, vol. XVI, pp. 389 f., where Savage is described as "the first clergyman who accepted 'evolution.'" Referring to him, the article continues: "While not the first American theologian to discern and to define the influence of the Darwinian hypothesis on religion, Savage was the first American preacher to attain such prominence and popularity as to bring the issue squarely and clearly to the attention of the Protestant world, especially its clergy . . . His persuasive and eloquent presentation of evolutionist propositions and corollaries, as well as those of Biblical criticism and comparative religion, performed an invaluable service in negotiating understanding and sympathy between Protestantism and science."

3 M. J. Savage, *The Religion of Evolution* (Boston, 1876), p. 23.
4 *Ibid.*, pp. 26 f.
5 *Ibid.*, p. 28.
6 *Ibid.*, pp. 43 f.
7 *Ibid.*, p. 83.
8 *Dictionary of American Biography*, vol. XVI, p. 390.
9 M. J. Savage, *op. cit.*, p. 51.
10 *Ibid.*, pp. 56, 63.
11 *Ibid.*, p. 63.
12 *Ibid.*, p. 81.
13 *Ibid.*, p. 82.
14 *Ibid.*, p. 51.
15 H. Brücher, *Ernst Haeckels Bluts- und Geisteserbe* (Munich, 1936), p. 91.
16 A. Ploetz, *Die Tüchtigkeit unserer Rasse und der Schutz der Schwachen*—an essay on racial hygiene and its relationship to humane ideals, particularly socialism (Berlin, 1895), p. 136.
17 A. Tille, *Volksdienst—Von einem Sozialaristokraten* (Berlin-Leipzig, 1893), p. 114.
18 Fritz Bolle, "Darwinismus und Zeitgeist," *Zeitschrift für Religions und Geistesgeschichte* XIV (1962), pp. 143 ff.
19 Ernst Haeckel. From the article: "Über unsere gegenwärtige Kenntnis vom Ursprung des Menschen" (1898), Gemeinverständliche Werke, vol. V, p. 371.
20 M. J. Savage, *op. cit.*, pp. 100 f.
21 *Ibid.*, p. 110.
22 *Ibid.*, p. 190.

23 *Ibid.*, p. 162.

24 On James McCosh, see *Dictionary of American Biography*, vol. XI, pp. 615 ff, and W. M. Sloane, *The Life of James McCosh* (1896), with autobiographical material and complete bibliography. We quote from the *Dictionary of American Biography:* "One of his most conspicuous contributions to philosophical and theological discussions during his early years at Princeton was in connection with the subject of evolution . . . In the early seventies, he stood out almost alone among the ministers of the United States, in defense of the doctrine of evolution . . . In an age when the discussion was just starting, he insisted that the doctrine of evolution was not directly or by implication, a denial of God, but that the program of evolution magnified the wonder and mystery of the process of creation."

25 James McCosh, *The Religious Aspect of Evolution* (New York, 1890), p. viii.

26 *Ibid.*, p. 101.

27 *Ibid.*, p. 110.

28 *Ibid.*, p. 113.

29 *Ibid.*, p. 119.

30 Concerning Henry Drummond, see G. A. Smith, *The Life of Henry Drummond.* New York, 1898. His doctrine of evolution is presented particularly in his work *The Ascent of Man* (3d ed.; New York, 1894). In its method of dealing with the subject, this work has wider scope than Teilhard de Chardin, inasmuch as the linguistic development of man is also dealt with as part of the process of cerebration. It also points to the accelerating effect of language in connection with evolution.

31 *The Ascent of Man*, p. 3.

32 *Ibid.*, pp. 2 f.

33 *Ibid.*, p. 9. Drummond introduced the terms Alpha and Omega into the description of the evolution of man. On pp. 115 f., Drummond describes man as the end of previous evolution and the beginning of a new kind of evolution. He concludes as follows: "Man was always told that his place was high; the reason for it he never knew till now; he never knew that his title deeds were the very laws of Nature, that he alone was the Alpha and Omega of Creation, the beginning and the end of Matter, the final goal of Life."

34 Henry Drummond, *Natural Law in the Spiritual World* (New York: Pott, 1904), p. 302.

35 *Ibid.*, p. 303.

36 *Ibid.*, pp. 389 f.

37 Concerning George Frederick Wright, see *Dictionary of American Biography*, vol. XX, pp. 550 f., and *Who's Who in America*, 1920–21.

38 Concerning Lyman Abbott, see *Dictionary of American Biography*, vol. I, p. 24. His principal work is *The Theology of an Evolutionist* (Cambridge: Riverside, 1897).

39 Among American scholars of his time he was also exceptional on account of his girth (300 lbs.). With reference to him, see *Dictionary of American Biography*, vol. VI, pp. 420 ff.; and J. S. Clark, *The Life and Letters of John Fiske* (1917); T. S. Perry, *John Fiske* (1906); F. C. Pierce, *Fiske and the Fiske Family* (1896).

40 In addition to Fiske, we should also mention Franklin Johnson (1836–1916), a Baptist minister, who published a work on *The Christian's Relation to Evolution* in 1904; even more important, in this connection, is Francis Howe Johnson for his work *What is Reality?* The author of this very remarkable book is not mentioned in the *Dictionary of American Biography*. Furthermore we have to refer to William Callyhan Robinson (1814–1911) who first belonged to the Episcopal and then to the Roman Catholic Church. In 1883, he published a book, anonymously, which was entitled *Clavis Rerum*. In it he "sought to reconcile the fundamentals of orthodoxy with the new ideas of science, then just becoming popularly known. Boldly, for that day, he declared therein that the law of life is a law of evolution" (*Dictionary of American Biography*, vol. XVI, pp. 56 f.).

41 The complete material on this trial can be found in: *Monkey Trial*, ed. by Sheldon Norman Grebstein. Boston. Houghton, 1960. In the Anti-Religious Museum in Moscow, a special room is reserved for the Tennessee trial.

42 Maximilian Jacta, *Berühmte Strafprozesse—Amerika*.

X

1 See Ernst Benz, *Schellings theologische Geistesahnen*. (Abhandlungen der Akademie der Wissenschaft und der Literatur, Mainz, 1955, no. 3.)

2 Concerning the formula *Deus ens manifestativum sui*, see Ernst Benz, *ibid.*, pp. 47 f.; also F. C. Oetinger, *Öffentliches Denkmal der Lehrtafel einer weil. Wirttembergischen Prinzessin Antonia*. Sämtliche Schriften II, vol. I (Stuttgart, 1958), pp. 18, 93, 118, 236, 267, etc. Also in *Theologia ex idea vitae deducta* (Frankfurt-Leipzig, 1765), pp. xxvi, xxvii, xxxi, etc.

3 The *physica sacra* is the principal theme of F. C. Oetinger's book, *Swedenborgs und anderer irdische und himmlische Philosophie zur Prüfung des Besten ans Licht gestellt*. Sämtliche Schriften Z, vol. II (Reutlingen, 1855); also in

his book, *Die Philosophie der Alten, wiederkommen in den gülden en Zeiten.* Frankfurt-Leipzig, 1762.

4 F. C. Oetinger, Preface of Hamberger to Oetinger's autobiography (Stuttgart, 1849), pp. x f.; see *Biblisches emblematisches Wörterbuch*, p. 407. Also *Biblisches Wörterbuch*, ed. by Hamberger. Stuttgart, 1849.

5 Concerning Adam being "struck" by the name of Jesus, see Jacob Boehme, "Von den drey Principien göttlichen Wesens," chap. II, no. 22, in *Alle göttlichen Schriften*, ed. by J. G. Gichtel (1715), vol. I, col. 478; "Von der Gnadenwahl," chap. 7, no. 16—vol. II, col. 2479; chap. 7, no. 30—vol. II, col. 2483; chap. 12, no. 8—vol. II, col. 2583.
    Boehme develops the term by an interpretation of Eph. I:4: "even as he chose us in him before the foundation of the world, that we should be holy and blameless before him."

6 Schelling, *Weltalter*, Works VIII, p. 205.

7 *Ibid.*, p. 206, see Psalm 118:22.

8 Karl Beth, *Der Entwicklungsgedanke und das Christentum* (Berlin, 1909), p. 126.

9 *Ibid.*, p. 98.

10 *Ibid.*, pp. 203, 214.

11 *Ibid.*, p. 261.

12 *Ibid.*, p. 268.

13 *Ibid.*, p. 269.

14 Edgar Dacqué, *Urwelt, Sage, Menschheit* (6th ed., 1931), p. 97; see Walter Zimmerman, *Evolution, Geschichte ihrer Probleme und Erkenntnisse* (Freiburg: Orbis Academicus, 1953), p. 485.

15 E. Dacqué, *op. cit.*, p. 98.

16 E. Dacqué, *Die Urgestalt* (Leipzig, 1940), p. 74; and *Vermächtnis der Urzeit* (1948), p. 193.

17 E. Dacqué, *Urwelt, Sage, Menschheit*, pp. 227 ff.

18 *Ibid.*, p. 107.

19 *Ibid.*, pp. 94 ff.

20 E. Dacqué, *Urgestalt*, p. 78.

21 *Ibid.*, pp. 139 f.

22 Leopold Ziegler, *Über die Welt des Organismus* (Leutstetten vor München, 1949), p. 22.

23 *Ibid.*, p. 54.

24 *Ibid.*, p. 87.

25 *Ibid.*, p. 84.

26 Leopold Ziegler, *Überlieferung* (Olten, 1948), pp. 371 ff.

27 Leopold Ziegler, *Lehrgespräch vom Allgemeinen Menschen* (Hamburg, 1956), p. 210.

28 *Ibid.*, pp. 221–31, 235.

29 *Ibid.*, p. 253.

XI

1 The Aurobindo Ashram in Pondicherry has a publishing house of its own which prints the English original works of Aurobindo, some of the foreign-language editions of his books and a number of Ashram periodicals. For the problem with which we are dealing here, we refer particularly to the periodical *The Advent*, a quarterly devoted to the exposition of Sri Aurobindo's Vision of the Future.

2 Sri Aurobindo, "Superman as a Product of Evolution" *Sri Aurobindo in Brief; A Collection of Thoughts and Aphorisms* (Pondicherry, 1959), p. 15.

3 *Ibid.*, p. 28.

4 *Ibid.*, p. 36.

5 *Ibid.*, p. 3.

6 Sri Aurobindo, *On Yoga*, vol. I: *The Synthesis of Yoga* (Pondicherry, 1955), p. 375. (Published in the United States by Associated Booksellers, 1960.)

7 *Letters of Sri Aurobindo* (1st series, 2d ed.; Pondicherry, 1950), p. 77.

8 Sri Aurobindo, *The Human Cycle* (Pondicherry, 1949), p. 278.

9 The remarks made by Aurobindo about the future evolution of man, which are found particularly in his works *The Life Divine, The Human Cycle*, and *The Synthesis of Yoga*, were collected, arranged in systematic order, and provided with commentaries in the volume: *Sri Aurobindo, The Future Evolution of Man*. New York: Humanities, 1964.

10 A somewhat superficial comparison of Teilhard and Sri Aurobindo can be found in André Monestier, *Teilhard et Sri Aurobindo*. Paris, 1963.

11 Letter of Aurobindo, dated 1932, in *Pioneer of the Supramental Age* (Sri Aurobindo Ashram, Delhi Branch, 1958).

12 Sri Aurobindo, *The Superman* (Pondicherry, 4th ed. 1950), p. 2. First published in the periodical *Arya* under the title: "The Type of the Superman," vol. I, no. 9 (April 1915).

There, Nietzsche is referred to as "the troubled, profound, half-luminous Hellenizing Slav." Aurobindo thus gives credence to Nietzsche's fanciful belief that he was a descendant of Polish aristocrats.

In connection with this topic, see Ernst Bertram, *Nietzsche* (Berlin, 1929), pp. 27 f.

13 According to Aurobindo's messianic self-interpretation, he has to carry the burden of supermanhood himself at first. See *Pioneer of the Supramental Age*, p. 64 (letter of 1911): "For the leader of the way, a work like ours has not only to bring down or represent and embody the Divine, but to represent,

too, the ascending element in humanity and to bear the burden of humanity to the full, and experience in grim earnest all the obstruction, difficulty, opposition, baffled, hampered and only slowly victorious labour which are possible on the path."

14 *The Superman*, p. 13.

15 *Ibid.*, p. 3.

16 *Ibid.*, p. 4.

17 *Sri Aurobindo, Thoughts and Aphorisms* (Sri Aurobindo Ashram, 1958), p. 22.

18 *The Superman*, p. 3.

19 See Ernst Benz, *Adam, Der Mythus vom Urmenschen*. Munich: O. W. Barth, 1955.

20 R. Graves, *Adam's Rib and Other Anomalous Elements in the Hebrew Creation Myth: A New View*. New York: British Book Service, 1955.

21 *The Superman*, pp. 12 f.

22 *Ibid.*, p. 6.

23 P. Chenchiah, "The Destiny of Man and the Interpretation of History," Supplement to *Madras University Journal*, XXIX, 1.

XII

1 The following scientific-critical research literature is available on Teilhard:

Claude Tresmontant, *Introduction à la pensée de Teilhard de Chardin*. Paris, 1956.

Claude Cuénot, *Pierre Teilhard de Chardin. Les grandes étapes de son évolution*. Paris: Plon, 1958—this is a comprehensive presentation of his life, his scientific work, and contains a complete bibliography of his works. (American edition: *Teilhard de Chardin: A Biographical Study*. Baltimore: Helicon, 1965.) By the same author: *Teilhard de Chardin, Ecrivains de Toujours*; Paris, 1962.

Georges Crespy, *La pensée théologique de Teilhard de Chardin*. Paris, 1961.

Paul Grenet, *Teilhard de Chardin, un évolutioniste chrétien*, in *Savants du monde entier*; Paris, 1961.

J. P. Blanchard, *Méthode et principes du Père Teilhard de Chardin*. Paris: La Colombe, 1961.

Nicolas Corte, *La vie et l'âme de Teilhard de Chardin*. Paris, 1957. (Available in English: *Pierre Teilhard de Chardin, His Life and Spirit*. New York: Macmillan, 1960.)

Henry de Lubac, *La pensée religieuse du Père Teilhard de Chardin*. Paris, 1962.

P. Mulders, *Het visieon von Teilhard de Chardin*. Brussels, 1962.

Charles E. Raven, *Teilhard de Chardin: Scientist and Seer*. New York: Harper, 1963.

Madeleine Barthélemy-Madaule, *Bergson et Teilhard de Chardin*. Paris, 1963.

2 Due to the circumstances of his life, there are few Germans among Teilhard's friends. One of them is the paleoanthropologist, Helmut de Terra, who describes his meetings with Teilhard and the latter's journeys of exploration in his book *Memories of Teilhard de Chardin*. New York: Harper, 1965.

3 *Geheimnis und Verheissung der Erde*, p. 62; October 1920, while traveling through Mongolia.

4 *Die Zukunft des Menschen*, p. 100. (Available in the United States: *The Future of Man* [New York: Harper, 1964].) "A passionate enjoyment of growth, of existence—this is what we need. Reject the faint-hearted, the skeptics, the pessimists and the melancholy, the tired and the immobile. Life is a perpetual discovery."

5 Thus in the *Lettres de voyage (1923–55)* (Peking, December 11, 1940), p. 265; and *Pilger der Zukunft*, p. 50. A translation of the first work is available in the United States: *Letters from a Traveller* (New York: Harper, 1962).

6 *Divinitas*, III.2 (Rome, 1959), 221, calls it *"dangereuse séduction"*; on p. 237 *"parfaitement détestable 'facilisme'"*; on p. 244 *"terrible aberration et séduction de facilité"*; on p. 363 *"non conciliabile in alcun modo col nostro patrimonio di fede."* The *Monitum* of the Holy Office of July 1962 states in connection with the philosophical and theological subject matter that the works (of Teilhard de Chardin) are "shot through with so many ambiguities and even with such serious errors that they are an insult to the Catholic doctrine." In the meantime, another issue of *Divinitas* was published, which was directed against Teilhard: "Teilhard et Teilhardisme," in the Quaderni di *Divinitas* III (1962), p. 75. One of the most outspoken Roman critics of Teilhard, Philippe de la Trinité, O.C.D., has now submitted his objections in a separate work: *Rome et Teilhard de Chardin* (Paris: Arthème Fayard, 1964). This work has the imprimatur of five Roman censorship authorities!

7 The demand for definite excommunication or, at least for putting some of the works of Teilhard de Chardin on the Index, has not ceased. See R. Teldy Naim, *Faut-il brûler Teilhard de Chardin?* Paris, 1964.

8 See, for example, his prayer in *Hymne de l'univers* (Paris, 1961), pp. 79 f., 163 f. (In English: *Hymn of the Universe* [New York: Harper, 1965].)

9 Of critical studies on Teilhard de Chardin, published during the

last few years, we have to mention particularly the following works:

Ignace Lepp, *Die neue Erde. Teilhard de Chardin und das Christentum in der modernen Welt.* Olten-Freiburg i B: Walter, 1962.

Hans-Éduard Hengstenberg, *Evolution und Schöpfung.* Munich: Anton Pustet, 1963.

Armin Müller, *Das naturphilosophische Werk Teilhard de Chardins.* Freiburg-Munich: Karl Alber, 1964.

10 *Geheimnis und Verheissung der Erde,* p. 210 (letter of September 8, 1935, on board the *Cathay*).

11 *Le groupe zoologique humain,* Les savants et le monde; (Paris: Albin Michel, 1956), p. 107.

12 In a letter to Maryse Choisy, see François-Albert Viallet, *Zwischen Alpha und Omega. Das Weltbild Teilhards de Chardin* (Nuremberg, 1959), p. 212.

13 "La fin de l'espèce," *Psyche* 76 (February 1953), in *L'avenir de l'homme,* p. 395.

14 *Ibid.,* p. 396.

15 Viallet, *op. cit.,* p. 188.

16 *Ibid.,* p. 72.

17 *Lettres de voyage* (1923–55), p. 302: "*à la poursuite du 'Dieu toujours plus grand.'*"

18 *Pilger der Zukunft,* p. 158 (letter from New York, February 28, 1954). See *Lettres de voyage* (1923–55), p. 354: "*le 'plus grand Christ.'*" Also *ibid.,* p. 48; and p. 97: "*la manifestation irréplaçable d'un plus grand Christ.*"

19 *Hymne de l'univers,* LVIII, p. 144 has a more probing text: "*Le Christ mystique n'a pas atteint sa pleine croissance, ni donc le Christ cosmique. L'un et l'autre, tout à la fois, ils sont et ils deviennent . . . Le Christ est le Terme de l'Evolution, même naturelle, des êtres; l'Evolution est sainte.'* The source referred to is "La vie cosmique," 24 mars 1916 (unpublished).

The text in *L'avenir de l'homme,* p. 397, does not contain the objectionable wording "*l'Evolution est sainte.*" The editor merely gave an excerpt from the article "La vie cosmique" and quite obviously trimmed it down. The objectionable juxtaposition of "*Christ mystique*" and "*Christ cosmique*" has also been removed. The "adjusted" text is the following: "*le Christ mystique n'a pas atteint sa pleine croissance. Le Christ est le Terme de l'Evolution même naturelle des êtres.*"

Quite unintentionally, two versions of the same text (which, as a whole, has not yet been edited) thus slipped into the official edition. Cases like this one show how important a critical edition would be, and how far removed the only available edition is from fulfilling this requirement.

20 *Lettres de voyage* (1923–55), p. 200: *"personnaliser le monde en Dieu"* (letter of January 24, 1936).

21 Cf. also, *ibid.*, *"s'il ne convergeait sur la Personne,"* and *Geheimnis und Verheissung der Erde*, p. 220 (letter of November 15, 1935).

22 Cf. also, *ibid.*, p. 351: *"à 'christifier' l'Evolution,"* and *Pilger der Zukunft*, p. 46 (letter from Peking, October 18, 1940), and p. 155 (letter from New York, November 8, 1953).

23 *Zukunft des Menschen*, p. 400.

XIII

1 Friedrich Heer, "Denker der Zukunft," a preface to François-Albert Viallet, *Zwischen Alpha und Omega. Das Weltbild Teilhards de Chardin* (Nuremberg, 1959), p. 9.

2 Heimo Dolch, "Erwägungen über die Aussage Teilhards de Chardin," *Catholica* 16, 2 (1962), p. 81; in a similar way, Heer reminds us of the trial of Jeanne d'Arc and its revision, and the 1835 revocation of the conviction of Galilei of 1616.

3 *Evolution after Darwin* (The University of Chicago Centennial; vol. II: *The Evolution of Man*). University of Chicago, 1960.

4 Teilhard, "La Messe sur le monde," *Hymne de l'univers*, pp. 17–19. (*Hymn of the Universe*, pp. 19 f.)

5 Jean Daniélou, "Gottes Wiederentdeckung; die Bedeutung Teilhard de Chardins für die Gegenwart," *Wort und Wahrheit* XVII, 8/9 (1962), p. 523.

6 On evil in the works of Teilhard, see
Armin Müller, *Das naturphilosophische Werk Teilhard de Chardins* (Freiburg/Munich), pp. 282 ff.
Madeleine Barthélemy-Madaule, *Bergson et Teilhard de Chardin* (Paris, 1963), pp. 411–21; 431–35; most of the works available until now keep silent on this subject.

7 Adolf Portmann, *Der Pfeil des Humanen. Über Teilhard de Chardin* (Freiburg/Munich, 1960), p. 60.

8 *Genèse d'une pensée. Lettres* (1914–19) (Paris: Grasset, 1961), p. 131 (letter of July 10, 1916).

9 *Ibid.*, p. 141 (letter of August 23, 1916): "At the sight of this place of bitter affliction, I was deeply moved that I had the honor to be present at one of the two or three points at which, in this hour, all life of the universe converges and recedes. These are painful points but—I believe in it more and more—a great future will emerge from here."

Ibid., p. 222 (letter of August 14, 1917): "For some time, I have felt seriously impelled to grab the problem of 'evil and progress' by the horns . . . My understanding in this regard may still be very limited. But perhaps I will think of the aesthetics of war, of which we talked to each other. For this it would be good, however, if I could breathe the strong atmosphere of the front line.—As always, after a long rest, I am gripped again by a longing for the front." On November 20, 1917, Teilhard completed a special publication on this subject under the title: *La nostalgie du front.*

In what direction his thoughts moved in connection with the mentioned problem of evil and progress, is shown in a sentence of his work *Le phénomène humain* (Appendice: "Quelques remarques sur la place et la part du mal dans un monde en évolution," p. 347): *"douleurs et fautes, larmes et sang: autant de sous-produits (souvent précieux, du reste, et ré-utilisables) engendrés en chemin par la noogénèse. Voilà donc en fin de compte, ce que, dans un premier temps d'observation et de réflexion, nous révèle le spectacle du Monde en mouvement."*

10 *Ibid.,* p. 140.

11 *Ibid.,* p. 222 (letter of February 15, 1917): "Believe me, I would prefer it a hundred times to throw hand grenades or handle a machine gun, rather than to be so useless. Maybe what I am telling you now is not very orthodox, but I still believe that there is a kernel of truth in it: It appears to me that this would be more in accord with my position as a priest. Isn't it the priest who has to bear the weight of life in its totality? Must he not show in his own person how human labor and love of God can be combined? . . . Actually, the question is rather theoretical since we are probably approaching the end of the war. But if we could start again from the beginning, I would act differently in December 1914."

12 Robert Jungk, *Brighter Than a Thousand Suns: The Fate of the Atomic Scientists.* New York: Harcourt, 1958.

13 *Zukunft des Menschen,* p. 187. Apparently Teilhard does not believe that Christianity is capable of holding man back from following this path.

14 *Ibid.,* p. 196.

15 *Ibid.,* "Ideas on Progress," pp. 87 ff.

16 *Ibid.,* p. 99.

17 *Ibid.,* pp. 203, 300, 314.

18 *Ibid.,* p. 326.

19 This is probably the point which provoked the criticism of reviewers representing the Curia. It is raised against him repeatedly. See article in *Divinitas* (1959), p. 238, which calls Teilhard *"le prophète qu'attendait notre siècle marxisé."* P. 241 adds: *"voilà, d'un coup d'aile, dépassé et assumé le marxisme, dont la plus profonde séduction n'est pas la 'lutte des classes,' mais bien l'affirmation de l'espérance qu'a*

*l'Homme de se construire lui-même collectivement par la
médiation de l'opus et de la factio."*

20 *L'avenir de l'homme*, p. 242. This "sympathy based on the mystical evidence of traveling together and finding each other
on the same summit" has never been extended to the Russian Orthodox or the Roman Catholic Church by the Communists in the states of the Eastern bloc, since they took
over power!

21 *Zukunft des Menschen*, p. 110. Already in his wartime letters
there are indications of presenting the contrasts in a harmless light and to reinterpret them as stages of evolution (see
letter of August 29, 1916, p. 141).

22 *Ibid.*, p. 185. These words were spoken in Peking under the impact of the progress of the Communist Revolution and the
march of Mao on Peking. The bourgeoisie is referred to unequivocally as "offal" and "scum," as the refuse-heap of
evolution. There are also other highly critical remarks of
Teilhard against the bourgeoisie, as *ibid.*, p. 397: "A time
of euphoria and abundance—a golden age—this, we are told,
is all that evolution has in store for us. Our heart is right in
rejecting such a 'petty-bourgeois' ideal."

23 *Ibid.*, p. 185; *L'avenir de l'homme*, pp. 174 f.

24 *Ibid.*, p. 183.

25 *Ibid.*, pp. 317 f.

26 *Ibid.*, pp. 177, 179.

27 How far removed *amorisation* is from Christian love of one's
fellowman in its simple, not intellectually diluted, sense, can
be seen in some of Teilhard's remarks which show a profound contempt for man. Cf. his wartime letters of September 8, 1918, and August 14, 1917.

28 Herder, *Auch eine Philosophie der Geschichte zur Bildung der
Menschheit*, Section 3, Zusätze. J. G. Herder, *Ideen zur
Kulturphilosophie* (Leipzig: Braun, 1911), p. 221.

29 Pascal, from his writings, selected and translated by Walter
Warnach (Düsseldorf: Pocket ed., No. 1, 1962), p. 9.

INDEX